HOW TO SOLVE CHEMISTRY PROBLEMS

COLES EDITORIAL BOARD

Bound to stay open

Publisher's Note

Otabind (Ota-bind). This book has been bound using the patented Otabind process. You can open this book at any page, gently run your finger down the spine, and the pages will lie flat.

ABOUT COLES NOTES

COLES NOTES have been an indispensible aid to students on five continents since 1948.

COLES NOTES are available for a wide range of individual literary works. Clear, concise explanations and insights are provided along with interesting interpretations and evaluations.

Proper use of COLES NOTES will allow the student to pay greater attention to lectures and spend less time taking notes. This will result in a broader understanding of the work being studied and will free the student for increased participation in discussions.

COLES NOTES are an invaluable aid for review and exam preparation as well as an invitation to explore different interpretive paths.

COLES NOTES are written by experts in their fields. It should be noted that any literary judgement expressed herein is just that – the judgement of one school of thought. Interpretations that diverge from, or totally disagree with any criticism may be equally valid.

COLES NOTES are designed to supplement the text and are not intended as a substitute for reading the text itself. Use of the NOTES will serve not only to clarify the work being studied, but should enhance the readers enjoyment of the topic.

ISBN 0-7740-3407-6

© COPYRIGHT 1998 AND PUBLISHED BY
COLES PUBLISHING COMPANY
TORONTO - CANADA
PRINTED IN CANADA

Manufactured by Webcom Limited
Cover finish: Webcom's Exclusive **DURACOAT**

CONTENTS

MEASUREMENT

I. THE METRIC SYSTEM

The metric system of measurement is used in all scientific calculations, and thus the mastery of this system is a necessity for all students of chemistry and physics. The metric system is the legal system of all countries except Unite : States and Great Britain. These two countries use the English system of measurement, and all of their engineers use this system. For this reason, it is often necessary to convert the English units into metric units and vice versa. This is very easily done for only one conversion factor need be memorized for each dimension, i.e., length, mass, and volume.

Learn the following relationships:

I. LENGTH

1 meter (m) = 100 centimeters (cm) = 1000 millimeters (mm)
1 kilometer (km) = 1000 m
1 micron (μ) = 10^{-4} cm
1 millimicron (mμ) = 10^{-7} cm
1 Angstrom (A) = 10^{-8} cm
    Conversion Factor: 2.54 cm = 1 inch

2. MASS

1 gram (g) is the mass of water which has a volume of 1 cubic centimeter (cc)
1 kilogram (kg) = 1000 g
1 gram = 1000 milligrams (mg)
    Conversion Factor: 1 lb = 454 g

3. VOLUME

1 cubic centimeter (cc) is the volume of a cube with its sides 1 centimeter long
1 cubic centimeter (cc) = 1 milliliter (ml) (approx.)
1 liter = 1000 ml
    Conversion Factor: 1 liter = 1.057 quarts
1 ml (cc) of water has a mass (or weight) of 1g
1 liter of water has a mass (or weight) of 1 kg

Note that for water only, if the mass is in grams the volume is the same number stated in milliliters: a mass of 438 g of water has a volume of 438 ml. Similarly, mass stated in kilograms and volume in liters are numerically the same: a volume of 6.28 liters of water has a mass of 6.28 kilograms.

Also note that in chemistry the terms "mass" and "weight" are often used as if they have the same meaning.

II. MEASUREMENT OF TEMPERATURE

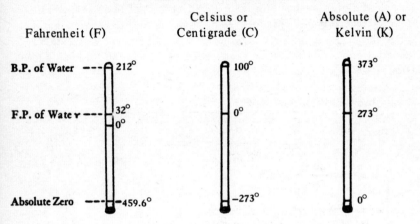

There are 180 degrees between the boiling point and freezing point of water on the Fahrenheit scale, whereas on the Centigrade scale there are 100 degrees. Thus a Fahrenheit degree is 5/9 of a Centigrade degree. Also since the freezing point of water is 32 degrees on the Fahrenheit scale, the conversion formulas are:

$$^{\circ}C = \frac{5}{9} \ (^{\circ}F - 32) \qquad\qquad ^{\circ}F = \frac{9}{5} \ ^{\circ}C + 32$$

$$^{\circ}A = {^{\circ}C} + 273$$

III. CONVERSION OF UNITS

Units as well as numbers undergo the processes of addition, subtraction, multiplication and division. Only objects having the same units (dimensions) may be added or subtracted directly. To add 4 quarts to 2 liters, one must be converted to the units of the other. When multiplying or dividing, the laws of algebra apply to the units the same as to the numbers.

$$2 \text{ in.} \times 3 \text{ in.} = 6 \text{ in.}^2$$

$$5 \frac{\text{miles}}{\text{hr}} \times 3 \text{ hr} = 15 \text{ miles} \qquad 3 \frac{\text{g}}{\text{cm}^3} \times 3 \text{ cm}^2 = 9 \frac{\text{g}}{\text{cm}}$$

EXAMPLES

1. Convert 3 feet to centimeters

Place the desired dimension of your answer to the left of the equality sign. On the right, put the given number and multiply by the conversion factors and units.

$$? \text{ cm} = 3 \, \cancel{ft} \cdot x \, \frac{12 \, \cancel{in}}{1 \, \cancel{ft}} \times \frac{2.54 \text{ cm}}{1 \, \cancel{in}}$$

$$= 3 \times 12 \times 2.54 \text{ cm}$$

$$= 91.4 \text{ cm}$$

2. Convert 30 mph to ft per sec.

$$? \frac{\text{ft}}{\text{sec}} = \frac{30 \, \cancel{miles}}{1 \, \cancel{hour}} \times \frac{1 \, \cancel{hr}}{60 \, \cancel{min}} \times \frac{1 \, \cancel{min}}{60 \text{ sec}} \times \frac{5280 \text{ ft}}{1 \, \cancel{mile}}$$

$$= 30 \times \frac{1}{60} \times \frac{1}{60 \text{ sec}} \times 5280 \text{ ft}$$

$$= \frac{44 \text{ ft}}{\text{sec}}$$

3. Convert 10 g per cm² to lbs per ft²

$$? \frac{\text{lbs}}{\text{ft}^2} = \frac{10 \, \cancel{g}}{1 \, \cancel{cm^2}} \times \frac{1 \text{ lb}}{454 \, \cancel{g}} \times \frac{(2.54)^2 \cancel{cm^2}}{(1)^2 \, \cancel{in^2}} \times \frac{(12)^2 \, \cancel{in^2}}{(1)^2 \, \cancel{ft^2}}$$

$$= 10 \times \frac{1 \text{ lb}}{454} \times 6.45 \times \frac{144}{1 \text{ ft}^2}$$

$$= 20.5 \text{ lbs per ft}^2$$

4. Convert 520 mg per ml to oz per qt

$$? \frac{\text{oz}}{\text{qt}} = \frac{520 \, \cancel{mg}}{1 \, \cancel{ml}} \times \frac{1 \, \cancel{g}}{1000 \, \cancel{mg}} \times \frac{1 \, \cancel{lb}}{454 \, \cancel{g}} \times \frac{16 \text{ oz}}{1 \, \cancel{lb}} \times \frac{1000 \, \cancel{ml}}{1 \, \cancel{liter}} \times \frac{1 \, \cancel{liter}}{1.057 \text{ qt}}$$

$$= 520 \times \frac{1}{1000} \times \frac{1}{454} \times \frac{16 \text{ oz}}{1} \times 1000 \times \frac{1}{1.057 \text{ qt}}$$

$$= 17.36 \text{ oz per qt}$$

5. Convert 77°F to °A

First convert to °C

$$^{\circ}\text{C} = \frac{5}{9} \, (^{\circ}\text{F} - 32) \qquad ^{\circ}\text{C} = \frac{5}{9} \, (77 - 32) \qquad ^{\circ}\text{C} = 25$$

Then convert to °A

$$^{\circ}\text{A} = ^{\circ}\text{C} + 273 \qquad ^{\circ}\text{A} = 25 + 273 \qquad ^{\circ}\text{A} = 298$$

6. Find the capacity in quarts of a container 2m long, 200mm wide and 20cm deep.

First convert all units to cm.

$$2m \times 100 \ \frac{cm}{m} = 200 \ cm.$$

$$200mm \times \frac{1}{10} \ \frac{cm}{mm} = 20 \ cm.$$

Volume of container $= 200 \ cm \times 20 \ cm \times 20 \ cm$

$$= 80,000 \ cm^3$$

Convert to quarts

$$? \ qt = 80,000 \ cm^3 \times \frac{1 \ liter}{1000 \ cm^3} \times \frac{1.057 \ qt}{1 \ liter}$$

$$= 84.6 \ qt$$

PROBLEMS

(ANSWERS ON PAGE 149)

1. Convert 10 inches to (a) cm (b) mm (c) m.

2. Convert 50 cm to (a) in (b) yds (c) ft.

3. Find the capacity in liters of a container 50 cm long, 0.2 m wide, and 20 mm deep.

4. Convert a pressure of 20 lbs per square inch to grams per square centimeter.

5. Convert 50 g to (a) mg (b) kg (c) lbs.

6. Convert 1 gallon to (a) liters (b) ml.

7. Convert 60 angstroms to (a) cm (b) in.

8. Convert (a) $68°F$ to $°C$ (b) $2°F$ to $°C$ (c) $182°F$ to $°C$.

9. Convert (a) $20°C$ to $°F$ (b) $50°C$ to $°F$ (c) $40°C$ to $°F$.

10. Convert (a) $-37°F$ to $°C$ (b) $-45°C$ to $°F$ (c) $-73°F$ to $°C$.

11. Convert (a) $112°C$ to $°A$ (b) $-40°C$ to $°K$ (c) $78°C$ to $°A$.

12. Convert (a) $1290°K$ to $°C$ (b) $301°A$ to $°C$ (c) $163°A$ to $°C$.

13. Convert 2.5 g per cm^3 to lb per in^3.

14. Convert 4 g per cm³ to lb per ft³.

15. Convert 60 miles per hr to km per sec.

16. Convert 100 microns to (a) millimicrons (b) cm (c) in.

17. Convert 10 in to (a) microns (b) millimicrons (c) Angstroms.

DENSITY AND SPECIFIC GRAVITY

I. DENSITY

Density is the mass of a substance contained in one unit volume of the substance.

$$\text{Density} = \frac{\text{mass of a substance}}{\text{volume of that substance}}$$

In the metric system the units of density are $\frac{g}{cm^3}$ or $\frac{g}{ml}$

In the English system the units of density are $\frac{lbs}{cu.\,ft}$

For gases, the units are usually $\frac{g}{\ell}$

The density of water at 4°C = $1\,\frac{g}{ml}$ = $62.4\,\frac{lbs}{cu.\,ft}$

II. SPECIFIC GRAVITY

Specific gravity is a ratio which denotes how much heavier a substance is than water.

$$\text{Sp. Gr.} = \frac{\text{Mass of a substance}}{\text{Mass of an equal volume of water at 4°C}}$$

If a substance has a specific gravity of 2, then it is twice as heavy as water. Specific gravity has no units; it is merely a ratio. Note that since 1 ml of water weighs 1 g, density and specific gravity are numerically equal in the metric system.

III. ARCHIMEDES' PRINCIPLE

Archimedes' Principle states that when a solid is immersed in a liquid the solid is buoyed up by a force equal to the weight of the liquid displaced.

Thus, a substance when partially or fully immersed in water will weigh less than it does in air. The apparent loss in weight equals the buoyant force which in turn equals the weight of the water displaced by the substance.

If a substance is fully immersed, it displaces a volume of liquid equal to its own volume. A substance with a volume of 28 ml will displace 28 ml of water, or gasoline, or air if the substance is fully in the fluid.

Note that a substance only displaces its own weight of liquid if it is floating.

The principle of Archimedes may be used to find the specific gravity or density of a substance.

EXAMPLES

1. A substance weighs 62.8 g in air and 34.2 g when fully immersed in water. Calculate the specific gravity of the substance.

   Buoyant force = apparent loss in weight = weight of water displaced = 62.8 - 34.2 = 28.6 g.

   Because the substance is fully under water, 28.6 g is the mass of water which has a volume equal to that of the solid.

   $$\text{Specific Gravity} = \frac{\text{mass of substance}}{\text{mass of an equal volume of water}} = \frac{62.8 \text{ g}}{28.6 \text{ g}}$$

   $$= 2.6$$

2. What is (a) the density (b) the specific gravity of a substance if it has a mass of 278.4 g and a volume of 32.0 ml?

   (a)
   $$\text{Density} = \frac{\text{Mass}}{\text{Volume}} = \frac{278.4 \text{ g}}{32.0 \text{ ml}} = \frac{8.7 \text{ g}}{\text{ml}}$$

   (b)
   The substance has a volume of 32.0 ml and an equal volume of water is 32.0 ml. This amount of water has a mass of 32.0 g.

   $$\text{Specific Gravity} = \frac{\text{mass of substance}}{\text{mass of an equal volume of water}} = \frac{278.4 \text{ g}}{32.0 \text{ g}}$$

   $$= 8.7$$

3. The density of silver is 655 lbs. per cubic foot. Calculate
   (a) the specific gravity (b) the weight of 100 ml of silver.

(a) Specific gravity = $\dfrac{\text{Mass of 1 cu. ft of silver}}{\text{Mass of 1 cu. ft of water}} = \dfrac{655\ lb}{62.4\ lb} = 10.5$

(b) The density of silver = 10.5 g/ml. Density and specific gravity are numerically equal in the metric system.

>   therefore 1 ml of silver weighs 10.5 g
>   100 ml weighs: $100 \times 10.5 = 1050$ g.

4. An aqueous solution of ammonia has a specific gravity of 0.909 and contains 25.48% ammonia by weight. Calculate (a) the number of grams of ammonia in 200 ml of solution (b) the volume of ammonia solution which includes 100 g of ammonia.

(a) One ml of solution weighs 0.909 g. Then 200 ml weighs $200 \times 0.909 = 181.8$ g

But the solution is only 25.48% ammonia by weight. Then $181.8 \times 0.2548 = 46.4$ g of ammonia.

(b) 0.909 g of ammonia solution has a volume of 1 ml and contains $0.2548 \times 0.909 = 0.232$ g of ammonia

0.232 g of ammonia in 1 ml solution

1 g of ammonia in $\dfrac{1}{0.232}$ ml solution

100 g of ammonia in $100 \times \dfrac{1}{0.232} = 431$ ml of solution

PROBLEMS

(ANSWERS ON PAGE 149)

1. Calculate (a) the density and (b) the specific gravity of a body that weighs 350 g and has a volume of 70 ml.

2. A substance has a volume of 200 ml and weighs 450 g. Calculate (a) the density and (b) the specific gravity.

3. A solid weighs 20 g in air and 12 g when immersed in water. Calculate the specific gravity of the solid.

4. A powder weighs 40 g in air. When added to 30 ml of water, the total volume is 45 ml. Calculate the specific gravity of the powder.

5. A container weighs 100 g when empty, 250 g when filled with water and 200 g when filled with an alcohol solution. Calculate

(a) the specific gravity of the alcohol solution, (b) the density of the alcohol solution.

6. Iron has a specific gravity of 7.6, gold 19.25. (a) What volume will 500 g of iron occupy? (b) What volume will 500 g of gold occupy? (c) How many cubic feet will 1000 lbs of gold occupy?

7. Determine the weight of 50 cubic feet of nickel. The density of nickel is 8.9 g/ml.

8. One cubic foot of platinum weighs 1330 lbs. Calculate (a) the specific gravity and (b) the weight of 200 ml of platinum.

9. The specific gravity of concentrated sulfuric acid solution is 1.86. Calculate (a) the weight of 500 ml of solution, (b) the density in g/ml, (c) the volume occupied by 500 g of the solution.

10. Concentrated sulfuric acid solution has a specific gravity of 1.86 and contains 95% sulfuric acid by weight. Calculate (a) the number of grams of sulfuric acid in 500 ml of solution, (b) the volume of acid solution which includes 50 g of acid.

11. The density of 58% glycerol solution in water is 1.15 g ml. Calculate the volume of this solution which includes (a) 500 g of glycerol, (b) 4 lbs of glycerol.

12. One thousand cubic feet of air weigh about 80 lbs. Calculate the density of air in grams per liter.

THE GAS LAWS

I. PRESSURE

Pressure is defined as force per unit area. It is usually expressed as $\frac{g}{cm^2}$, $\frac{lbs}{in^2}$, atmospheres, or millimeters of mercury. Atmospheric pressure may be measured by means of a barometer. A simple barometer may be constructed by completely filling with mercury a tube which is more than 800 mm long, closed at one end. The tube

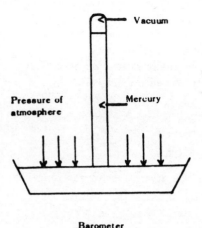

Vacuum

Mercury

Pressure of atmosphere

Barometer

is then carefully inverted by placing the open end in a shallow vessel which contains mercury in such a manner so that no air is permitted to enter the tube. The mercury in the tube will drop, creating a vacuum, until it reaches a height where the pressure exerted by the mercury in the tube will exactly equal the pressure of the atmosphere on the surface of the exposed mercury. Since the pressure of the atmosphere varies from day to day and also with the altitude, the pressure of the atmosphere at sea level has been averaged and found to be equal to the pressure exerted by a column of mercury 760 mm high. This pressure has been designated as 1 atmosphere.

II. STANDARD CONDITIONS

Standard conditions (Standard Temperature and Pressure, or STP) have been designated as a temperature of $0°C$ ($273°A$) and a pressure of 760 mm of mercury (1 atm). Since the volume and density of a gas vary with the temperature and pressure it is frequently necessary to convert all gases to standard conditions for purposes of comparison.

III. CHARLES' LAW

The volume occupied by a given mass of a gas at different temperatures is directly proportional to the absolute temperature of the gas, pressure remaining constant.

EXAMPLE

1. A mass of gas at standard conditions occupies 5 liters. What volume will this gas occupy at $200°C$ if the pressure is constant? Since we are using Charles' law the temperatures must be stated in the absolute temperature scale.

V_1 = 5 liters V_2 = ? liters

$T_1 = 0°C = 273°A$ $\xrightarrow{\text{increases}}$ $T_2 = 200°C + 273° = 473°A$

The temperature is increased and the gas will have a bigger volume. Gases expand on heating and contract on cooling. The new volume will be the original volume multiplied by a ratio of temperatures. In this case, the temperature ratio must be greater than 1 so that the new volume will exceed the old value.

$$V_2 \text{ liters} = 5 \text{ liters} \times \frac{473°A}{273°A} = 8.7 \text{ liters}$$

IV. BOYLE'S LAW

At constant temperature, the volume of a given mass of gas is inversely proportional to the pressure.

EXAMPLE

1. A mass of gas at standard conditions occupies a volume of 10 liters. What volume will the gas have at a pressure of 4.6 atmospheres if the temperature remains constant?

$V_1 = 10$ liters $\qquad\qquad V_2 = ?$ liters

$P_1 = 1$ atm $\xrightarrow{\text{increases}} P_2 = 4.6$ atm

Increased pressure makes a gas smaller in volume. Therefore, in this example, the new volume will be the original volume multiplied by a ratio of pressures smaller than 1. This will give a final volume smaller than the original volume.

$$V_2 \text{ liters} = 10 \text{ liters} \times \frac{1 \text{ atm}}{4.6 \text{ atm}} = 2.2 \text{ liters}$$

V. COMBINED GAS LAW

EXAMPLE

1. A mass of gas occupies 500 ml at 327°C and 1200 mm pressure. Calculate the volume of this gas at 22°C and 700 mm pressure.

$V_1 = 500$ ml $\qquad\qquad V_2 = ?$ ml

$P_1 = 1200$ mm $\xrightarrow{\text{decreases}} P_2 = 700$ mm

$T_1 = 327°C + 273 \xrightarrow{\text{decreases}} T_2 = 22°C + 273$

$\quad = 600°A \qquad\qquad\qquad = 295°A$

new volume = original volume × pressure ratio × temperature ratio.

Decreased pressure allows the gas molecules to move apart and occupy a bigger volume. Thus, the pressure ratio will be greater than 1. Decreased temperature, or cooling a gas makes its volume smaller. The temperature ratio will be smaller than 1.

$$V_2 \text{ ml} = 500 \text{ ml} \times \frac{1200 \text{ mm}}{700 \text{ mm}} \times \frac{295^\circ\text{A}}{600^\circ\text{A}} = 421 \text{ ml}$$

VI. VARIATION IN DENSITY

EXAMPLE

1. The density of a gas is 1.43 g per liter at STP. Calculate the density of the gas in g per liter at 80°C and 4 atm pressure. This problem may be solved in two stages:

   (a) If 1 liter is taken as the original volume of the gas, the mass of this quantity is known (1.43 g) and it must contain a definite, very large number of molecules. Altering the pressure and temperature will give a new volume of gas which still has the same number of molecules and therefore the same mass, 1.43 g.

   (b) The general gas law is applied to find the volume V_2 which will have the same mass as V_1.

   Then the weight of 1 liter of gas at the new conditions is readily calculated.

   (a) $V_1 = 1$ liter $\qquad\qquad\qquad V_2 = ?$ liters

   $P_1 = 1$ atm $\xrightarrow{\text{increases}}$ $P_2 = 4$ atm

   $T_1 = 0°C = 273°A \xrightarrow{\text{increases}} T_2 = 80°C + 273 = 353°A$

   the mass of the amount of gas being considered is 1.43 g and is not affected by the pressure and temperature changes

   $$V_2 \text{ liters} = 1 \text{ liter} \times \frac{1 \text{ atm}}{4 \text{ atm}} \times \frac{353^\circ\text{A}}{273^\circ\text{A}} = 0.323 \text{ liters}$$

   (b) If 0.323 liters of gas has a mass of 1.43 g

   1 liter has a mass of $\dfrac{1.43}{0.323} = 4.42$ g

   Density of the gas is 4.42 g per liter

Note that a similar method may be used in this problem:
At 20°C and 740 mm pressure, 460 ml of a gas weighs 1.84 g. Calculate the weight of 200 ml of the gas at 176°C and 960 mm pressure.

18

V_1 is 460 ml and whatever value is calculated for V_2 will have a weight of 1.84 g. Again, because the number of molecules is constant.

(a) V_2 ml = 460 ml × $\dfrac{740 \text{ mm}}{960 \text{ mm}}$ × $\dfrac{449°A}{293°A}$ = 543 ml

(b) If 543 ml of gas weighs 1.84 g

1 ml of gas weighs $\dfrac{1.84}{543}$ g

200 ml of gas weighs 200 × $\dfrac{1.84}{543}$ = 0.68 g

Errors in gas law problems may be avoided if these points are kept in mind:

1. Convert temperatures to the absolute scale.
2. Increased pressure and increased temperature have the opposite effect on the volume of a gas.

Increased pressure makes the gas volume smaller.
Increased temperature makes the gas volume greater.

VII. OTHER APPLICATIONS OF THE GENERAL GAS LAW

Simultaneous changes in the volume and temperature of a gas produce a change in pressure.

new pressure = original pressure × volume factor × temperature factor

Decreasing the volume will increase the pressure. The same number of molecules in a smaller space will make more collisions per second with the interior walls of the container and thus raise the pressure.

Decreasing the temperature makes the kinetic energy of the molecules less. They slow down and exert less pressure on the container walls.

If the volume and the pressure of a gas are changed it will have a new temperature.

Increased pressure raises the kinetic energy and therefore the thermal energy and temperature. Similarly a decreased volume raises the temperature.

new temperature = original temperature × pressure factor × volume factor

VIII. DALTON'S LAW OF PARTIAL PRESSURES

The total pressure exerted by a mixture of gases is the sum of the individual pressures exerted by the constituent gases taken separately.

This principle must be considered when a gas is collected over water. The total pressure exerted by a gas collected over water will be equal to the partial pressure of the gas itself plus the partial pressure of the water vapor. Since the partial pressure of the water vapor is definite for each temperature, it is necessary only to subtract the vapor pressure of water at the temperature which it is collected from the total pressure in order to get the partial pressure of the collected gas. (See appendix for a table of vapor pressures of water.)

EXAMPLES

1. Exactly 200 ml of nitrogen were collected over water at 30°C and 780 mm. Calculate the volume that the dry nitrogen would occupy at standard conditions. The vapor pressure of water at 30°C = 31.51 mm. The collected nitrogen is saturated with water vapor. The partial pressure of the water vapor at 30°C = 31.51 mm. The partial pressure of nitrogen = 780 − 31.51 = 748.49 mm.

$V_1 = 200$ ml $V_2 = ?$ ml

$P_1 = 748.5$ mm $\xrightarrow{\text{increases}}$ $P_2 = 760$ mm

$T_1 = 30°C + 273° \xrightarrow{\text{decreases}} T_2 = 0°C + 273° = 273°A$

$\quad = 303°A$

The pressure ratio will be less than 1, because increased pressure makes the volume smaller. Similarly, the temperature ratio will be less than 1, because lowering the temperature makes the volume less.

$$V_2 \text{ ml} = 200 \text{ ml} \times \frac{748.5 \text{ mm}}{760 \text{ mm}} \times \frac{273°A}{303°A} = 177.8 \text{ ml}$$

IX. PROBLEMS

(ANSWERS ON PAGE 150)

1. A mass of gas occupies 40 liters at 0°C and 740 mm. Calculate the volume of the gas at STP.

2. A mass of gas occupies 300 ml at 0°C and 760 mm. Calculate the volume of this gas at 0°C and 740 mm.

3. A mass of gas occupies 500 ml at 27°C and 760 mm. Calculate the volume of this gas at STP.

4. A mass of gas occupies 200 ml at -10°C and 1 atm. Calculate the volume of this gas at STP.

5. A mass of gas occupies 80 liters at 40°C and 780 mm. Calculate the volume of this gas at 0°C and 4 atm.

6. A mass of gas occupies 1250 ml at -27°C and 790 mm. Calculate the volume of this gas at STP.

7. A gas in a sealed tube exerts a pressure of 380 mm at 20°C. What is the pressure of this gas at 80°C?

8. A gas in a sealed tube exerts a pressure of 2 atm at 100°C. What is the pressure of this gas at 20°C?

9. Five hundred ml of oxygen were collected over water at 25°C and 765 mm. Calculate the volume that the dry oxygen would occupy at STP.

10. One thousand ml of hydrogen were collected over water at 18°C and 750 mm. Calculate the volume that the dry hydrogen would occupy at STP.

11. The density of a gas is 1.43 $\frac{g}{\ell}$ at STP. Calculate the density of the gas at 27°C and 740 mm.

12. The density of a gas is 0.09 $\frac{g}{\ell}$ at 10°C and 760 mm. Calculate the density of this gas at STP.

13. A mass of 32 g of oxygen at STP occupies 22.4 liters. Calculate the weight of 20 liters of oxygen at 10°C and 740 mm.

14. A one liter container holds 0.36 g of helium at STP. What mass of helium will this container hold at 50°C and 4 atm?

FORMULAS OF COMPOUNDS AND NOMENCLATURE

I. THE VALENCE NUMBER (OXIDATION NUMBER)

When elements combine to form compounds, they gain, lose or share electrons. The valence number or oxidation number is the number of electrons gained, lost or shared. Any atom which loses electrons has a positive valence number corresponding to the fact that loss of negative electrons leaves behind a positively charged atom (ion).

sodium atom, Na − 1 electron ⟶ Na^+ ion
the valence number of sodium is + 1.

magnesium atom, Mg − 2 electrons ⟶ Mg^{2+} ion
the valence number of magnesium is + 2.

Similarly, any atom gaining one or more electrons will form a negatively charged ion, and the oxidation number is negative with a value equal to the number of electrons gained.

oxygen atom, 0 + 2 electrons ⟶ 0^{2-} ion
the valence number of oxygen is - 2.

In cases where electrons are shared, atoms may have positive or negative oxidation numbers which do not indicate gain or loss of electrons. The positive and negative valence numbers are used as part of the rules for writing correct formulas. For example, carbon has a valence number of + 4, but does not give up four electrons.

BINARY COMPOUNDS

A binary compound contains only two elements combined chemically. Water H_2O, sodium chloride NaCl, propane gas C_3H_8 are examples.

Some Rules

In a binary formula

(a) the first written element has a positive valence number, and the second element has a negative valence number

(b) metals always have a positive valence number

(c) the sum of all the positive and negative valence numbers is zero in a correct formula

22

+1	+2	+3	+4	+5
H Hydrogen	Ba Barium	Al Aluminum		
Na Sodium	Mg Magnesium	As Arsenic (III) arsenious		As Arsenic (V) arsenic
K Potassium	Ca Calcium	Sb Antimony (III) antimonous		Sb Antimony (V) antimonic
Ag Silver	Zn Zinc	P Phosphorus (III) phosphorous		P Phosphorus (V) phosphoric
Cu Copper (I) cuprous	Cu Copper (II) cupric	Bi Bismuth (III) bismuthous		Bi Bismuth (V) bismuthic
Hg Mercury (I) mercurous	Hg Mercury (II) mercuric			
	Fe Iron (II) ferrous	Fe Iron (III) ferric	C Carbon	
	Cr Chromium (II) chromous	Cr Chromium (III) chromic	Si Silicon	
	Sn Tin (II) stannous		Sn Tin (IV) stannic	

-1	-2
F Fluorine	O Oxygen
Cl Chlorine	S Sulfur (in sulfides)
Br Bromine	
I Iodine	

EXAMPLES OF BINARY FORMULAS

Binary compounds have the name ending —IDE

Name of first element + part of name of second element + ide

silver + oxygen ⟶ silver oxide

sodium + chlorine ⟶ sodium chloride

1. Sodium Na, valence number + 1 with chlorine, Cl, valence number - 1 forms the compound sodium chloride, formula NaCl. The sum of the valence numbers + 1 -1 = 0.

2. Calcium Ca, valence number + 2, combines with oxygen 0, valence number - 2 to form the compound calcium oxide, formula Ca0. 1 atom of each element gives a valence sum of zero, + 2 - 2 = 0.

3. If aluminum chloride is taken as an example, the correct formula must contain Al with valence number + 3, and Cl with valence number - 1. Then 3 Cl atoms with a total valence of $3 \times (-1) = -3$ balance 1 Al atom with valence number + 3. $+3 -3 = 0$ Aluminum chloride is $AlCl_3$.

PROBLEMS

(ANSWERS ON PAGE 150)

1. Write formulas for (a) sodium bromide (b) potassium chloride (c) magnesium sulfide (d) calcium fluoride (e) aluminum iodide.

2. Name the substances with formulas (a) AgI (b) Na_2O (c) $ZnBr_2$ (d) BaS (e) Al_2O_3.

II. SOME ALTERNATIVE NAMES

The table of valence numbers shows that copper, iron, and other elements have two oxidation numbers. It follows that copper forms two different oxides, iron forms two different chlorides and so on. To distinguish the compounds the name endings -ous and -ic are used.

cuprous oxide Cu_2O has copper with valence number + 1
cupric oxide CuO has copper with valence number + 2

The two iron chlorides are

ferrous chloride $FeCl_2$ the iron has valence number + 2
ferric chloride $FeCl_3$ the iron has valence number + 3

RULE: the -ous ending is used with the lower valence number, and the -ic ending with the higher value.

A more modern system of naming is shown by these examples: copper (II) oxide, iron (III) chloride, mercury (I) sulfide, antimony (V) oxide. The Roman numeral in parenthesis, (I), (II), (III) etc., refers to the valence number of the element written in front.

Phosphorus (III) oxide P_2O_3 has $P = +3$ and $0 = -2$

Tin (IV) fluoride SnF_4 has $Sn = +4$ and $F = -1$

PROBLEMS

(ANSWERS ON PAGE 150)

1. Write formulas for (a) cupric chloride (b) stannous fluoride (c) antimony (III) bromide (d) ferric sulfide (e) mercury (II) oxide.

2. Give two acceptable names for the compounds with these formulas (a) FeO (b) PCl_3 (c) HgI (d) Sb_2O_5 (e) CuCl.

III. A SHORT ROUTE TO BINARY FORMULAS

As binary formulas are worked out, a simple "cross-over" rule is seen to apply in general:

sodium chloride $\qquad \underset{Na}{+1} \times \underset{Cl}{-1} \qquad \longrightarrow \qquad$ NaCl

aluminum bromide $\qquad \underset{Al}{+3} \times \underset{Br}{-1} \qquad \longrightarrow \qquad AlBr_3$

iron (III) oxide $\qquad \underset{Fe}{+3} \times \underset{0}{-2} \qquad \longrightarrow \qquad Fe_2O_3$

phosphoric sulfide $\qquad \underset{P}{+5} \times \underset{S}{-2} \qquad \longrightarrow \qquad P_2S_5$

Ignore the positive and negative signs. Simply switch the valence numbers and write them just below and after the other symbol.

Special cases occur in magnesium sulfide

$\underset{Mg}{+2} \times \underset{S}{-2} \qquad \longrightarrow \qquad$ MgS but not Mg_2S_2

and tin (IV) oxide

$\underset{Sn}{+4} \times \underset{0}{-2} \qquad \longrightarrow \qquad SnO_2$ but not Sn_2O_4

Valence number ratios of this type are simplified:

2 : 2 becomes 1 : 1   2 : 4 becomes 1 : 2

Peroxides discussed later are exceptions.

The same simple "cross-over" rule may be used with non-binary formulas as shown in later sections, provided that the valence numbers of the radicals are known.

IV. SOME SPECIAL CASES

Hydrides. Hydrogen has a valence number of - 1 in binary compounds called hydrides, where the element is combined with metals above it in the activity series. Examples are sodium hydride NaH, calcium hydride CaH_2.

Sulfur Oxides. In sulfur dioxide SO_2, sulfur has a valence number + 4, and in sulfur trioxide SO_3 the S is +6.

Peroxides. Oxygen has valence number - 1 instead of - 2 in peroxides.

When the formulas of some oxides and the corresponding peroxides are compared, it is seen that the peroxides have one more oxygen atom than is found in the oxides.

Oxide	Peroxide
sodium oxide Na_2O	sodium peroxide Na_2O_2 (Not NaO)
potassium oxide K_2O	potassium peroxide K_2O_2
barium oxide BaO	barium peroxide BaO_2

Molecules of Elements. Some elements occur as units called molecules in which two or more of the same atoms are combined by sharing electrons.

Examples: oxygen O_2 hydrogen H_2 nitrogen N_2

fluorine F_2 chlorine Cl_2 bromine Br_2

iodine I_2 ozone O_3 phosphorus P_4

V. FORMULAS OF ACIDS

BINARY ACIDS. There are binary acids with names of this type

Hydro + name of element + ic + the word acid

Hydrochloric acid HCl	Hydrobromic acid HBr
Hydriodic acid HI	Hydrosulfuric acid H_2S

These acids are formed when gases with the same formulas as the acids dissolve in water and react chemically with it. The gases are hydrogen chloride HCl, hydrogen bromide HBr, hydrogen iodide HI, and hydrogen sulfide H_2S.

OXYGEN ACIDS. The key element in all acids is hydrogen. Acids in water solution release hydrogen ions H^+ (really hydronium ions H_3O^+). Many acids contain oxygen and have names of this type

name of element + (ous or ic) + the word acid

Nitric acid HNO_3	Nitrous acid HNO_2
Chloric acid $HClO_3$	Chlorous acid $HClO_2$

Rule: the name of an oxygen acid ending in -ous has one less oxygen atom than the corresponding acid with name ending -ic.

Other rules apply in the naming of acids.

Chlorous acid $HClO_2$	Hypochlorous acid $HClO$
Bromous acid $HBrO$	Hypobromous acid $HBrO$

Rule: the prefix hypo- is used in naming an oxygen acid which has one less oxygen atom than the corresponding -ous acid.

There are also oxygen acids with one more oxygen atom than the acid with name ending -ic.

Chloric acid' $HClO_3$	Perchloric acid $HClO_4$
Iodic acid HIO_3	Periodic acid HIO_4

Rule: the prefix per- is used in naming an oxygen acid which has one more oxygen atom than the corresponding acid with name ending -ic.

HALOGEN OXY-ACIDS. The halogen family fluorine F, chlorine Cl, bromine Br, iodine I, and the new element astatine At, show close similarities in their properties and in the formulas of their acids. The name rules applied to chloric acid, perchloric acid etc. are used with the corresponding acids of the other halogens.

Chloric acid $HClO_3$	Fluoric acid HFO_3
Hypochlorous acid $HClO$	Hypobromous acid $HBrO$

ACID RADICALS. All acid-forming molecules react with water to release hydrogen ions (actually hydronium ions H_3O^+). The remaining negatively charged part of the acid is called the acid radical. Whether it consists of one atom or several, the acid radical is considered as a unit with a definite negative valence number. Also, the acid radical exists as a unit in the salts derived from the various acids.

Acid		Acid Radical	
Nitric acid	HNO_3	Nitrate	NO_3^-
Chloric acid	$HClO_3$	Chlorate	ClO_3^-
Acetic acid	CH_3COOH	Acetate	CH_3COO^-
Formic acid	$HCOOH$	Formate	$HCOO^-$

Each of these acid radicals has a valence number of -1, and carries a surplus negative charge, -1. Since hydrogen has a valence number +1, loss of a hydrogen ion H^+ by each acid forming molecule must leave a radical with a valence number -1 to keep the rule that the sum of the valence numbers in a formula is zero.

$$HNO_3 \longrightarrow H^+ + NO_3^-$$

Rule: if the name of the oxygen acid ends in -ic, the acid radical has name ending -ate.

OTHER ACIDS AND THEIR ACID RADICALS

Acid		Acid Radical		Radical Valence Number
Perchloric acid	$HClO_4$	Perchlorate	ClO_4^-	-1
Chlorous acid	$HClO_2$	Chlorite	ClO_2^-	-1
Hypochlorous acid	$HClO$	Hypochlorite	ClO^-	-1
Sulfuric acid	H_2SO_4	Sulfate	SO_4^{2-}	-2
Sulfurous acid	H_2SO_3	Sulfite	SO_3^{2-}	-2
Carbonic acid	H_2CO_3	Carbonate	CO_3^{2-}	-2
Silicic acid	H_2SiO_3	Silicate	SiO_3^{2-}	-2
Phosphoric acid	H_3PO_4	Phosphate	PO_4^{3-}	-3
Phosphorous acid	H_3PO_3	Phosphite	PO_3^{3-}	-3

Note that each acid radical has a valence number equal to the number of hydrogens lost as H^+ from the acid molecule. Also, each radical has a charge of the size written above the radical.

Example: SO_4^{2-} has two extra electrons and therefore a charge of -2.

Another naming rule is that if an oxygen acid has name ending -ous, the acid radical has name ending -ite.

Also, Hypo..... ous acids give Hypo....... ite radicals

and   Per...... ic acids give Per. .... ate radicals

Examples: Hypobromous acid HBr0 gives the Hypobromite radical
             BrO^-.   Periodic acid HIO_4 gives the Periodate radi-
             cal IO_4^-.

SALTS

Salts are composed of positively charged metal ions such as Na^+, Mg^{2+}, Fe^{3+} and others, chemically combined with the various negatively charged acid radicals such as NO_3^-, ClO_4^-, CO_3^{2-}.

All salts called nitrates, contain the NO_3^- radical in common but differ in the kind of positive metal ion.

Similarly since chloric acid yields the chlorate radical by loss of hydrogen ion from the acid molecule, salts such as sodium chlorate, calcium chlorate and other chlorates contain the ClO_3^- ion in common.

A salt may be regarded as the substance formed by replacing the hydrogen atoms of the acid molecule by positive metal ions (or by the ammonium ion, NH_4^+, discussed later).

    Positive metal ion + Negative acid radical ⟶ Salt

The "cross-over" rule may be used to write formulas of salts.

Sodium nitrate $\overset{+1}{Na} \overset{-1}{\underset{}{\times}} NO_3$ ⟶ $NaNO_3$

                  nitrate
                  radical

Silver chlorate $\overset{+1}{Ag} \overset{-1}{\underset{}{\times}} ClO_3$ ⟶ $AgClO_3$

                  chlorate
                  radical

Calcium nitrate $\overset{+2}{Ca} \overset{-1}{\underset{}{\times}} NO_3$ requires 1 Ca with 2 NO_3

radicals, to give a total valence sum of zero. We write $Ca(NO_3)_2$

Similarly, tin (IV) chlorate $\overset{+4}{Sn} \overset{-1}{\underset{}{\times}} ClO_3$ ⟶ $Sn(ClO_3)_4$

Keeping the 4 chlorate units in parenthesis indicates that 1 Sn is chemically united to 4 chlorate radicals each containing 1 Cl and 3 0 atoms, a total of 1 Sn 4 Cl and 12 0 atoms in the formula.

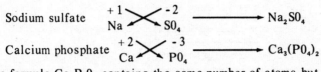

The formula $Ca_3P_2O_8$ contains the same number of atoms but is not quickly recognized as being a phosphate. For this reason the acid radical unit is kept in parenthesis.

EXERCISE

(ANSWERS ON PAGE 150)

1. Write formulas for (a) potassium chlorate (b) silver carbonate (c) calcium sulfate (d) mercury (I) phosphate (e) ferric sulfate (f) aluminum perchlorate (g) barium formate

2. Give names for (a) Na_2CO_3 (b) $CuSO_4$ (c) $KBrO_4$ (d) $Zn(ClO_2)_2$ (e) $AlPO_3$ (f) $As_3(PO_4)_5$.

SOME OTHER CASES

A. Hydrogen carbonate (bicarbonate) radical

Loss of 2 H^+ ions from one carbonic acid molecule yields the carbonate radical $H_2CO_3 \longrightarrow 2 H^+ + CO_3^{2-}$

The molecule may break down in this way instead
$H_2CO_3 \longrightarrow H^+ + HCO_3^-$ (hydrogen carbonate or bicarbonate) radical

Similarly, sulfuric acid

$H_2SO_4 \longrightarrow 2 H^+ + SO_4^{2-}$ (sulfate radical)

$H_2SO_4 \longrightarrow H^+ + HSO_4^-$ (hydrogen sulfate or bisulfate) radical

Sulfurous acid H_2SO_3 gives the sulfite SO_3^{2-} and the hydrogen sulfite (bisulfite) HSO_3^- radical.

Three different acid radicals are obtainable from phosphoric acid, H_3PO_4. They are phosphate PO_4^{3-} dihydrogen phosphate $H_2PO_4^-$ and monohydrogen phosphate HPO_4^{2-}.

Examples: calcium hydrogen carbonate

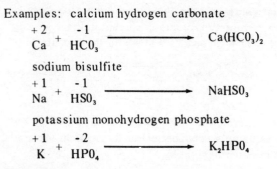

$$\overset{+2}{Ca} + \overset{-1}{HCO_3} \longrightarrow Ca(HCO_3)_2$$

sodium bisulfite

$$\overset{+1}{Na} + \overset{-1}{HSO_3} \longrightarrow NaHSO_3$$

potassium monohydrogen phosphate

$$\overset{+1}{K} + \overset{-2}{HPO_4} \longrightarrow K_2HPO_4$$

B. Hydroxides

Water is H_2O or HOH. The molecule may split to give 1 H^+ ion and 1 OH^- ion or radical. Hydroxides are compounds containing a positive metal ion combined with the hydroxyl ion or radical OH^- which has a valence number of -1.

$$\text{sodium hydroxide } \overset{+1}{Na} + \overset{-1}{OH} \longrightarrow NaOH \text{ sodium hydroxide}$$

$$\text{iron (II) hydroxide } \overset{+2}{Fe} + \overset{-1}{OH} \longrightarrow Fe(OH)_2$$

C. Ammonium and Ammonia

Ammonia is a gas with formula NH_3. When this gas reacts chemically with water or acids, the positive ion or radical NH_4^{+1} is formed, and may form salts with acid radicals as in these examples

$$\text{ammonium chloride } NH_4^{+1} + \overset{1-}{Cl} \longrightarrow NH_4Cl$$

$$\text{ammonium sulfate } NH_4^{+1} + \overset{-2}{SO_4} \longrightarrow (NH_4)_2SO_4$$

$$\text{ammonium hydrogen carbonate } NH_4^{+1} + \overset{-1}{HCO_3} \longrightarrow NH_4HCO_3$$

USE OF GREEK PREFIXES

Sometimes certain elements have too many valence numbers to be designated by the ous and ic endings. In these cases Greek prefixes are used to indicate the subscripts.

mono	=	1	tetra = 4
sesqui	=	1.5	penta = 5
di	=	2	hexa = 6
tri	=	3	hepta = 7

Examples

CrO = Chromium monoxide (chromous oxide) or chromium (II) oxide

Cr_2O_3 = Chromium sesquioxide (chromic oxide) or chromium (III) oxide

CrO_3 = Chromium trioxide

CrO_4 = Chromium tetraoxide

Three names are acceptable for formulas such as

P_2O_3	phosphorous oxide		phosphoric oxide
	phosphorus trioxide	and P_2O_5	phosphorus pentoxide
	phosphorus (III) oxide		phosphorus (V) oxide

Note the distinction between phosphorus – the name of the element and phosphorous – the name used when the element is showing its valence number + 3.

PROBLEMS

(ANSWERS ON PAGE 150)

1. Write formulas for the binary compounds formed by

   (a) sodium and iodine
   (b) potassium and oxygen
   (c) calcium and bromine
   (d) carbon and chlorine
   (e) silver and sulfur.

2. Name

   (a) AgCl
   (b) MgI_2
   (c) $SnBr_2$
   (d) $FeCl_3$
   (e) HgBr
   (f) Cu_2O

3. Write formulas for

   (a) phosphorus (III) bromide
   (b) iron (II) chloride
   (c) arsenic (V) oxide
   (d) copper (II) sulfide
   (e) cupric oxide
   (f) mercuric oxide
   (g) bismuth (III) iodide
   (h) stannic oxide

4. Determine the valence number of the first element in these formulas

   (a) KI
   (b) Ag_2S
   (c) ZnO
   (d) Fe_2O_3
   (e) SnS
   (f) PF_5
   (g) PF_5
   (h) MnO_2

5. Write formulas for

   (a) sodium hydroxide
   (b) calcium hydroxide
   (c) aluminum hydroxide

   (d) stannous hydroxide
   (e) tin (IV) hydroxide
   (f) iron (II) hydroxide

6. Write formulas for

   (a) oxygen
   (b) ozone
   (c) nitrogen
   (d) phosphorus

   (e) hydrogen peroxide
   (f) barium peroxide
   (g) hydrogen chloride

7. Name

   (a) KOH
   (b) $Zn(OH)_2$

   (c) $Al(OH)_3$
   (d) $Sn(OH)_4$

   (e) $Fe(OH)_3$
   (f) $Ba(OH)_2$

8. Name

   (a) HI
   (b) H_3PO_3

   (c) HNO_3
   (d) H_2SO_3

   (e) $HClO_3$
   (f) $HClO_4$

9. Write formulas for

   (a) hydrobromic acid
   (b) phosphoric acid
   (c) nitric acid

   (d) sulfuric acid
   (e) hypochlorous acid
   (f) chlorous acid

10. Name

    (a) $(NH_4)_2SO_3$
    (b) $FeSO_3$

    (c) Cu_2SO_4
    (d) $Sn(NO_3)_2$

    (e) $Fe_3(PO_4)_2$
    (f) $Fe(ClO_2)_2$

11. Write formulas for

    (a) ferric sulfate
    (b) cupric sulfite
    (c) ammonium nitrite
    (d) stannic phosphate

    (e) ferric phosphate
    (f) copper (I) oxide
    (g) iron (II) fluoride
    (h) tin (IV) oxide

12. Write formulas for

    (a) chromic sulfate
    (b) chromium (II) iodide
    (c) ammonium nitrate
    (d) mercuric sulfate

    (k) copper (II) sulfate
    (l) barium carbonate
    (m) potassium silicate
    (n) potassium perchlorate

(e) mercury (I) oxide
(f) zinc carbonate
(g) calcium silicate
(h) magnesium nitrate
(i) aluminum sulfide
(j) cuprous oxide

(o) iron (II) chlorate
(p) silver phosphate
(q) silver chlorate
(r) sodium hypochlorite
(s) potassium nitrate
(t) sodium nitrite

13. Name

(a) $(NH_4)_2SO_4$
(b) $(NH_4)_3PO_4$
(c) $CuSO_4$
(d) Ag_2O
(e) Ag_3PO_4
(f) SnO
(g) Hg_2O

(h) $ZnSO_4$
(i) Na_2SO_3
(j) NH_4OH
(k) CO_2
(l) CO
(m) ZnS
(n) $Al(OH)_3$

(o) $NaClO_2$
(p) $KClO$
(q) $CaSiO_3$
(r) $NaClO_4$
(s) $ZnSiO_3$
(t) HgI_2

14. (a) hydrogen ion
(b) hydronium ion
(c) sodium ion
(d) magnesium ion
(e) sulfide ion
(f) ferrous ion
(g) chloride ion
(h) copper (I) ion

(i) oxide ion
(j) manganese (II) ion
(k) chlorate ion
(l) bisulfite ion
(m) ammonium ion
(n) hydrogen carbonate ion
(o) fluoride ion
(p) phosphate ion

ATOMIC WEIGHT, MOLECULAR WEIGHT AND MOLES

I. ATOMIC WEIGHTS

Atom weights of the elements are the relative weights of the atoms of the elements based on the carbon-12 isotope weighing 12.0000. Sodium has atomic weight 23, indicating that one sodium atom is almost twice the mass of a carbon atom. Helium with atomic weight 4, is made of atoms which are one third the weight of the carbon atom. It follows that if the actual mass of the carbon-12 atom in grams is known, the absolute mass in grams of any other atom may be found. For example, a mercury atom weighs in grams 200/12 of the weight in grams of the carbon-12 atom because the relative atomic weights are mercury 200 and carbon 12.

II. GRAM-ATOMS, GRAM ATOMIC WEIGHT AND THE MOLE

The terms gram-atom, gram atomic weight and mole all represent the same quantity of an element.

Oxygen has atomic weight 16. Its gram atomic weight is 16 grams. 1 gram-atom of oxygen is 16 g and 1 mole of oxygen atoms is also 16 g.

Examples

1. How many grams are present in 4.0 moles of aluminum?

Atomic weight of Al = 27. Thus 1 mole (1 gram-atom, 1 gram atomic weight) of Al = 27 g.
4.0 moles of Al = $4.0 \times 27 = 108$ g

2. How many moles are present in 13.8 g of sodium?

Atomic weight of sodium = 23   1 mole (gram-atom, 1 gram atomic weight) of Na = 23 g

$$23 \text{ g of Na} = 1 \text{ mole}$$

$$1 \text{ g of Na} = \frac{1}{23} \text{ mole}$$

$$13.8 \text{ g of Na} = \frac{13.8 \times 1}{23} = 0.6 \text{ mole of sodium}$$

In these examples the term mole is being used to represent a specific mass of the element.

1 mole of an element = atomic weight of the element (in gram units)

The term mole is also used as a count of particles. 1 mole of any species contains 6.02×10^{23} particles of that species.

1 mole of oxygen atoms $= 16$ g $= 6.02 \times 10^{23}$ oxygen atoms

1 mole of mercury $= 200$ g $= 6.02 \times 10^{23}$ mercury atoms

Examples

1. How many atoms are in 5.0 moles of calcium?

Atomic weight of Ca = 40   Thus 1 mole of Ca is 40 g

1 mole of Ca contains 6.02×10^{23} Ca atoms

5.0 moles contain $5.0 \times 6.02 \times 10^{23} = 30.1 \times 10^{23}$ (or 3.01×10^{24}) Ca atoms

2. What is the mass in grams of 1 aluminum atom?

Atomic weight of Al = 27   1 mole of Al = 27 g

1 mole of Al = 6.02×10^{23} Al atoms weigh 27 g

1 Al atom weighs $\dfrac{27}{6.02 \times 10^{23}}$ = 4.49×10^{-23} g

3. How many moles are represented by 9.82×10^{25} atoms of an element? Note that there is no need to name the element or use its atomic weight.

1 mole of an element = 6.02×10^{23} atoms

9.82×10^{25} atoms represent $\dfrac{9.82 \times 10^{25}}{6.02 \times 10^{23}}$ = 1.63×10^2 moles

4. What is the weight in grams of 1.806×10^{24} atoms of carbon?

1 mole = 6.02×10^{23} atoms = 12 g of carbon

1.806×10^{24}C atoms = $\dfrac{1.806 \times 10^{24}}{6.02 \times 10^{23}}$ = 3.0 moles of carbon

1 mole of carbon weighs 12 g   3 moles weigh 36 g

Avogadro's Number

6.02×10^{23} is called Avogadro's number

III. AMU, ATOMIC MASS UNITS

Instead of stating atomic weights as numbers C = 12, Na = 23, Hg = 200 etc. the unit of atomic mass may be used. Then the atomic weight of carbon-12 is 12 atomic mass units or 12 amu, the atomic weight of sodium is 23 amu, mercury 200 amu and so on.

It follows that 1 amu is $\dfrac{1}{12}$ of the mass in grams of a carbon-12 atom.

Experimentally the amu is found to be 1.66×10^{-24} g.

Conversion Factor: 1 amu = 1.66×10^{-24} g

EXAMPLES

1. What is the mass in grams of 1 calcium atom?

Atomic weight of calcium = 40 amu

1 amu = 1.66×10^{-24} g

40 amu = $40 \times 1.66 \times 10^{-24}$ = 6.64×10^{-23} g

2. What is the atomic weight of an element if 1 atom weighs 1.24×10^{-22} g? Identify the element.

$$1.66 \times 10^{-24} \text{ g} = 1 \text{ amu}$$
$$1.24 \times 10^{-22} \text{ g} = \frac{1.24 \times 10^{-22}}{1.66 \times 10^{-24}} = 75 \text{ amu}$$

Atomic weight of the element is 75 amu, it is arsenic.

IV. FORMULA WEIGHT, MOLECULAR WEIGHT AND THE MOLE

The formula weight or molecular weight is obtained by adding all the atomic weights of the atoms in a formula.

Examples

1. Water, H_2O atomic weight of H = 1, atomic weight of O = 16

$$
\begin{array}{lll}
2 \text{ H} & 2 \times 1 = & 2 \\
1 \text{ O} & 1 \times 16 = & 16 \\
\end{array}
$$

molecular weight
(formula weight) $= 18$ amu

2. Sodium carbonate, Na_2CO_3. Atomic weights are Na = 23, C = 12, and O = 16

$$
\begin{array}{lll}
2 \text{ Na} & 2 \times 23 = & 46 \\
1 \text{ C} & 1 \times 12 = & 12 \\
3 \text{ O} & 3 \times 16 = & 48 \\
\end{array}
$$

formula weight
(molecular weight) $= 106$ amu

3. In calculating the formula weight of a hydrate such as copper (II) sulfate pentahydrate, $CuSO_4.5H_2O$ care is needed with the $.5H_2O$ part which means 5 water molecules attached to 1 $CuSO_4$ unit.

Atomic weights are Cu = 63.5, S = 32, O = 16, H = 1

$$
\begin{array}{llll}
 & 1 \text{ Cu} & 1 \times 63.5 = & 63.5 \\
 & 1 \text{ S} & 1 \times 32 = & 32 \\
\text{Note:} & 4 \text{ O} & 4 \times 16 = & 64 \\
5H_2 & 10 \text{ H} & 10 \times 1 = & 10 \\
\text{and } 5O & 5 \text{ O} & 5 \times 16 = & 80 \\
\end{array}
$$

formula weight $= 249.5$ amu

As with the terms gram-atom and gram atomic weight for elements, corresponding terms gram formula weight and gram molecular weight are used with the formulas for elements and compounds. For example,

Water, formula H_2O, formula weight $(2 \times 1) + 16 = 18$
    gram formula weight = 18 g = 1 mole of the compound

Sodium carbonate, Na_2CO_3, formula weight $(2 \times 23) + (1 \times 12) + (3 \times 16) = 106$
    gram formula weight = 106 g = 1 mole

Oxygen, formula O_2, formula weight $2 \times 16 = 32$
    gram formula weight = 32 g = 1 mole of oxygen molecules.

EXAMPLES

1. What is the weight in grams of 18 moles of sulfuric acid?

    Formula H_2SO_4 Atomic weights H = 1, S = 32, O = 16

    formula weight $(2 \times 1) + (1 \times 32) + (4 \times 16) = 98$ amu

    1 mole = gram formula weight = 98 g

    18 moles of H_2SO_4 $18 \times 98 = 1764$ g

2. How many moles are represented by 4.8 g of sodium hydroxide?

    Formula NaOH   Atomic weights Na = 23, O = 16, H = 1

    formula weight $23 + 16 + 1 = 40$ amu

    1 mole of NaOH = 40 g   4.8 g is $\frac{4.8}{40} = 0.12$ moles

The meaning of mole does not have to be restricted to the number of atoms of an element or the number of molecules of a compound.

    1 mole Na atoms = 6.02×10^{23} Na atoms

    1 mole of water = 6.02×10^{23} H_2O molecules each containing 2 H atoms and 1 O atom

    1 mole sulfate ion = 6.02×10^{23} SO_4^{2-} ions each containing 1 S atom with 4 O atoms and 2 extra electrons

    1 mole of electrons = 1 faraday = 6.02×10^{23} electrons

V. PROBLEMS

(ANSWERS ON PAGE 151)

1. Calculate the number of moles in (a) 40 g Ca, (b) 30 g C,
   (c) 500 g Fe, (d) 20 g As.

2. How many grams are represented by (a) 3 moles of S, (b) 0.15
   moles of Zn, (c) 4.8 moles of Co, (d) 0.01 moles of Al?

3. Calculate the number of atoms in 0.2 moles of tin.

4. What is the mass in grams of 1 atom of fluorine?

5. What weight in grams is represented by 20 amu?

6. 1 atom of an element weighs 9.12×10^{-23} g. Calculate the atomic
   weight of the element and identify it.

7. Calculate the molecular weight of (a) SF_6, (b) H_3PO_4, (c) C_4H_{10}

8. Calculate the formula weight of (a) $Ca(OH)_2$, (b) $Al_2(SO_4)_3$,
   (c) $MgSO_4.7H_2O$, (d) $Na_2Cr_2O_7$.

9. How many moles are there in (a) 500 g of NaOH, (b) 90 g of CH_4,
   (c) 142 g of Cl_2, (d) 3.0 g of CH_3COOH?

10. How many grams are represented by (a) 1.25 moles of HNO_3,
    (b) 2.4 moles of $BaSO_4$, (c) 0.02 moles of KOH, (d) 15 moles of
    $(NH_4)_3PO_4$?

11. How many molecules are in 0.3 moles of propane, C_3H_8?

12. How many sodium atoms are in 8 moles of sodium peroxide, Na_2O_2?

PERCENTAGE COMPOSITION AND CALCULATION OF FORMULAS

I. FRACTION AND PERCENTAGE COMPOSITION

Pure compounds are composed of many simple units which are represented by the formulas of the compounds. Water is made of many
millions of molecules written as H_2O. Common salt (sodium chloride)
is given the formula NaCl because it is composed of a very large
number of Na^+ ions and Cl^- ions in the ratio 1 Na^+ : 1 Cl^-.

In water the ratio is

$$\frac{1 \text{ O atom}}{1 \text{ H}_2\text{O molecule}} \text{ which by weight is } \frac{16 \text{ amu}}{18 \text{ amu}} \text{ or } \frac{0.889}{1}$$

Thus oxygen is 0.889 parts of a unit weight of water.

1 g of water contains 0.889 g of oxygen and $1 - 0.889 = 0.111$ g H
  In 100 g of water, $100 \times 0.889 = 88.9$ g oxygen
  and $100 \times 0.111 = 11.1$ g hydrogen

Examples

1. Calculate the percentage composition of potassium chlorate, $KClO_3$
   The atomic weights are K = 39, Cl 35.5, O = 16
   The formula weight of $KClO_3$ = 122.5 amu

   The fraction weights are $K = \frac{39}{122.5}$ $Cl = \frac{35.5}{122.5}$ $O = \frac{3 \times 16}{122.5}$

   $\%K = \frac{39}{122.5} \times 100$ $\%Cl = \frac{35.5}{122.5} \times 100$ $\%O = \frac{48}{122.5} \times 100$

   $= 31.8\%$ $= 29.0\%$ $= 39.2\%$

2. Calculate the percentage water in bluestone crystals, $CuSO_4.5H_2O$
   Atomic weights are Cu = 63.5 S = 32 H = 1 O = 16
   The formula weight of the compound = 249.5 (calculated on page 36)

   fraction of water $= \frac{5 \text{ H}_2\text{O}}{CuSO_4.5H_2O}$ by weight $= \frac{5 \times 18}{249.5}$

   $\%H_2O = 100 \times \frac{90}{249.5} = 36.1$

In these examples the percentage composition is calculated from the formulas and the atomic weights of the elements.

The known formula of a compound is not required for the calculation of the percentage composition by weight.

Example. A 10.4 g sample of a compound is found to contain 1.36 g of magnesium and 9.04 g of bromine. Calculate the percentage composition of the compound.

Fraction of Mg $= \frac{1.36 \text{ g}}{10.4 \text{ g}}$ Fraction of Br $= \frac{9.04 \text{ g}}{10.4 \text{ g}}$

$= 0.1305$ $= 0.8695$

$\%Mg = \frac{1.36}{10.4} \times 100$ $\%Br = \frac{9.04}{10.4} \times 100$

$= 13.05\%$ $= 86.95\%$

II. CALCULATION OF
FORMULAS

I. Empirical (Simplest) Formulas

The empirical or simplest formula indicates the relative number of atoms in the smallest whole number ratio.

Water H_2O is the actual molecular formula. H_2O is also the simplest formula.

Sodium peroxide Na_2O_2 is the actual formula
$\quad\quad\quad\quad\quad$ NaO is the simplest or empirical formula

Acetic acid CH_3COOH or $C_2H_4O_2$ is the actual molecular formula
$\quad\quad\quad\quad$ CH_2O is the simplest formula

The simplest formula may or may not represent the actual molecular formula of a compound. For example, there is no substance with formula NaO, but CH_2O is the molecular formula of a compound (not acetic acid) as well as being the simplest formula for acetic acid.

2. Molecular Formulas

The molecular or true formula indicates the actual number of atoms in the molecule. Thus C_6H_6 is the true formula for benzene, its smallest molecular unit able to exist independently has 6 C atoms combined chemically to 6 H atoms. The simplest formula of benzene is CH, which also happens to be the simplest formula of a different compound, acetylene C_2H_2. Thus it is possible for substances with different molecular formulas to have the same empirical formula.

3. Empirical Formula from the Weight Composition of the Compound

Any set of weight compositions of a compound such as
(a) an oxide of iron contains 14 lb. iron combined with 4 lb. oxygen
(b) the percentage weight composition of sodium sulfate is 32.4%Na, 22.53%S and 45.06%O.
(c) 1 gram of a compound contains 0.522 g C, 0.0131 g H, and 0.4649 g O may be used to find the empirical formula.

The weight of an element in a compound will depend on the relative atomic weight of its atom and the number of its atoms in the simplest formula of the compound. Divide the weight of each element by its atomic weight. This yields the relative number of moles of each element or the ratio of the atoms in the simplest formula. The ratio is converted to a simple whole number proportion.

EXAMPLES

1. Calculate the empirical formula of a compound which contains 3.6 g of carbon combined with 1.2 g of hydrogen.

	Carbon	Hydrogen
Weight Composition	3.6 g	1.2 g
Atomic Weights	12	1

$$\text{Ratio of Atoms} \qquad \frac{3.6}{12} \quad : \quad \frac{1.2}{1} = 0.3 \; : \; 1.2$$

Atoms are chemically indivisable, so that a formula $C_{0.3}H_{1.2}$ can not exist. However, the ratio 0.3 : 1.2 is the simple whole number ratio 1 : 4.

The empirical formula of the compound is CH_4.

2. Calculate the simplest formula of a compound which on analysis gave the following percentage composition by weight

$$Pb = 64.1\% \quad Cr = 16.1\% \quad O = 19.8\%$$

The actual weight units are not required to solve the problem as long as the relative weights of each element in a sample are known.

	Lead	Chromium	Oxygen
Weight Comp.	64.1	16.1	19.8
Atomic Weights	207.2	52	16

$$\text{Ratio of Atoms} \qquad \frac{64.1}{207.2} \quad : \quad \frac{16.1}{52} \quad : \quad \frac{19.8}{16}$$

$$0.309 \quad : \quad 0.309 \quad : \quad 1.236$$

The smallest whole number ratio is obtained by dividing each term in the ratio by the smallest number, 0.309.

$$\frac{0.309}{0.309} : \frac{0.309}{0.309} : \frac{1.236}{0.309} = 1 : 1 : 4$$

The empirical formula is then $PbCrO_4$

3. The formula of a hydrate may be calculated in a similar manner. A 12.00 g sample of a hydrate $ZnCl_2 . XH_2O$ was found to contain 3.4 g of water. Calculate the empirical formula of the hydrate. Note that it is not necessary to convert the weights to percentage values. Atomic weights are Zn = 65, Cl = 35.5, H = 1, O = 16
Weight of $ZnCl_2$ = 12.00 - 3.4 = 8.6 g

	$ZnCl_2$	H_2O
Weight Comp.	8.6 g	3.4 g
Formula Weight	136	18

$$\text{Ratio of Molecules} \quad \frac{8.6}{136} \; : \; \frac{3.4}{18} \; = \; 0.063 \; : \; 0.189$$

$$\frac{0.063}{0.063} \; : \; \frac{0.189}{0.063} \; = \; 1 \; : \; 3$$

The empirical formula is $ZnCl_2.3H_2O$

Avoiding Errors

A. Dividing the weight of each element by its atomic weight may give a ratio of atoms such as $1 : 1 : 2.5$ or $1 : 1.5 : 3.5$

In such cases it is necessary to multiply each term in the ratio by 2.

$$1 : 1 : 2.5 \; = \; 2 : 2 : 5$$

and $\quad 1 : 1.5 : 3.5 = 2 : 3 : 7$

B. A ratio of atoms such as $1 : 1.33$ should not be rounded off to $1 : 1$ or $1 : 1.5$

Multiply the ratio terms by 1, 2, 3 etc., and inspect the resulting ratios to find one closest to a simple whole number ratio

$$1 : 1.33 \; = \; 2 : 2.66 \; = \; 3 : 3.99 \; = \; 4 : 5.32 \; = \; 5 : 6.65$$

$3 : 4$ is the ratio wanted

III. TRUE (MOLECULAR) FORMULAS FROM EMPIRICAL FORMULAS

The examples of benzene C_6H_6 and acetylene C_2H_2 with the same empirical formula, illustrate the fact that the true (molecular) formula is not known by a simple inspection of the empirical formula.

The actual formula weight of the compound must be known.

$$\frac{\text{molecular formula weight of benzene}}{\text{empirical formula weight}} = \frac{C_6H_6}{CH} = \frac{78}{13} = 6$$

molecular formula C_6H_6 = (empirical formula) $\times$ 6

$$\frac{\text{molecular formula weight of acetylene}}{\text{empirical formula weight}} = \frac{C_2H_2}{CH} = \frac{26}{13} = 2$$

molecular formula C_2H_2 = (empirical formula) $\times$ 2

EXAMPLES

1. The empirical formula of a compound is CH_3O, and the true formula weight is 62. Calculate the true molecular formula.

   empirical formula weight is $12 + (3 \times 1) + 16 = 31$

   The true formula weight is just twice the simplest formula weight.

   Therefore, molecular formula $= (CH_3O) \times 2 = C_2H_6O_2$

2. A compound has a formula weight of 46 and a simplest formula C_2H_6O. Calculate the true molecular formula.

   Empirical formula weight $= (2 \times 12) + (6 \times 1) + (1 \times 16)$

   $$= 46$$

   This is the same as the true formula weight.

   Therefore the true formula is C_2H_6O.

IV. PROBLEMS

(ANSWERS ON PAGE 152)

1. A 24 g sample of NaI is found to contain 3.67 g of Na and 20.33 g of I. Calculate (a) the fraction weight of each element in the compound and (b) the percentage of each element.

2. A sample of K_3PO_4 is found to contain 27.76 g K, 7.36 g P, and 15.18 g O. Calculate (a) the weight fraction of each element present and (b) the percentage composition.

3. Calculate the percentage composition of (a) Na_2O, (b) KOH, (c) $AgClO_3$, (d) $Pb(NO_3)_2$, (e) $C_6H_4Cl_2$.

4. What is the percentage water of hydration in $Na_2CO_3.10H_2O$?

5. Calculate the empirical formula of a compound with weight composition: S = 21.9%, F = 78.1%.

6. Calculate the simplest formula of a compound which on analysis had the weight composition: 39.1% C, 8.7% H, and 52.2% O.

7. 0.521 g of a chloride of phosphorus contains 0.0775 g of phosphorus. Calculate the empirical formula of the compound.

8. A compound has composition 87.5% N, and 12.5% H. Its molecular weight is 32. Calculate (a) the simplest formula, (b) the molecular formula.

9. Calculate the molecular formula of a compound which is 47.4% S and 52.6% Cl. The molecular weight is 135.

10. A compound has empirical formula CHO_2. If its true formula weight is 90 calculate the molecular formula.

11. Cyclopropane has the molecular formula C_3H_6. What is its molecular formula weight and its empirical formula?

12. When 8.00 g of a hydrate of potassium fluoride, $KF.XH_2O$ is heated, 3.06 g of water is lost. Calculate the formula of the hydrate.

EQUATIONS, TYPES OF CHEMICAL REACTIONS, ACTIVITY SERIES

I. MEANING AND BALANCING OF EQUATIONS

When magnesium is burned in oxygen, magnesium oxide is formed. Magnesium and oxygen are called the reactants. Magnesium oxide is the product of the reaction. In writing an equation, the formulas of all reactants are put to the left of the arrow, and the formulas of all products are placed at the right hand side.

Reactants ⟶ Products

In addition to showing the correct formulas of all the substances, the total number of each kind of atom on the left must also appear on the right. The law of Conservation of Matter applies to chemical changes, no atoms are created or destroyed.

Mg + O ⟶ MgO   correct balance of atoms, but a wrong formula, oxygen has formula O_2 and not O.

Mg + O_2 ⟶ MgO   correct formulas, but incorrect balance of atoms. Two O atoms on the left must reappear on the right. Balancing by altering the numbers of atoms may only occur by changing the numbers in front of the formulas, so that the formulas remain correct.

The correct equation balanced is
2Mg + O_2 ⟶ 2MgO   This indicates that 2 Mg atoms react with 1 oxygen molecule to produce 2 identical units of the compound, each consisting of 1 Mg united to 1 O.

In a trial and error method of balancing equations, there are some
rules which help. A later section (page 74) shows how to use
valence number method in balancing equations more systematically.

Rules

1. All formulas of reactants and products must be correct.

2. Balance numbers of atoms only by changing numbers in front of
   formulas.

3. Start the balancing with an element which appears only in one
   formula on each side. For example, if oxygen is in two reactants
   and several products do not attempt balancing the equation by
   starting with the oxygen atoms.

4. Treat a radical such as NH_4 or SO_4 as a unit if the radical is
   in a reactant and a product.

EXAMPLE Balance the equation:

$$Al + H_2SO_4 \longrightarrow Al_2(SO_4)_3 + H_2$$

All formulas are correct. 2 Al atoms are needed on the left

$$2Al + H_2SO_4 \longrightarrow Al_2(SO_4)_3 + H_2$$

3 SO_4 radicals on the right require 3 H_2SO_4 molecules on the left.

$$2Al + 3H_2SO_4 \longrightarrow Al_2(SO_4)_3 + H_2$$

Finally, 6 atoms of H on the left require 3 H_2 molecules on the right
for balance.

$$2Al + 3H_2SO_4 \longrightarrow Al_2(SO_4)_3 + 3H_2$$

PROBLEMS

(ANSWERS ON PAGE 152)

Balance these equations (all formulas are correct)

(a) $KClO_3 \longrightarrow KCl + O_2$
(b) $HgO \longrightarrow Hg + O_2$
(c) $P + Cl_2 \longrightarrow PCl_5$
(d) $FeCl_2 + Cl_2 \longrightarrow FeCl_3$
(e) $Ca(OH)_2 + HNO_3 \longrightarrow Ca(NO_3)_2 + H_2O$
(f) $Zn + H_3PO_4 \longrightarrow Zn_3(PO_4)_2 + H_2$

II. TYPES OF CHEMICAL REACTIONS

A large number of chemical reactions may be classed as these types:

> combination, decomposition, displacement
> double decomposition, neutralization

(1) COMBINATION

Elements or compounds unite chemically to form one product.

$$Fe + S \longrightarrow FeS$$
$$CaO + CO_2 \longrightarrow CaCO_3$$

(2) DECOMPOSITION

A compound breaks down into two or more elements or compounds. Frequently heat is used to cause the reaction (thermal decomposition)

$$2Ag_2O \longrightarrow 4Ag + O_2$$
$$2KClO_3 \longrightarrow 2KCl + 3O_2$$
$$2Pb(NO_3)_2 \longrightarrow 2PbO + 4NO_2 + O_2$$

(3) DISPLACEMENT

An element reacts with a compound to replace and set free one of the elements in the compound.

a. active metal + an acid

$$Mg + H_2SO_4 \longrightarrow MgSO_4 + H_2$$

A solution of an acid is broken into ions. Therefore, this displacement is better represented by

$$Mg + 2H^+ + SO_4^{2-} \longrightarrow Mg^{2+} + SO_4^{2-} + H_2$$

The magnesium atom has given up two electrons which are gained by the H^+ ions of the acid. The salt produced, magnesium sulfate, remains as separate ions in water solution.

b. active metal + salt of a less active metal (in solution)

$$Fe + CuCl_2 \longrightarrow FeCl_2 + Cu$$

Again, a better representation of the reaction may be given. The $CuCl_2$ in solution exists as separate ions with charges equal to the valence numbers of the ions Cu^{2+} and Cl^-. The displacement is really the more active iron atom giving up two electrons to the less active Cu^{2+} ion. The Cl^- plays no direct part and is called a "spectator" ion.

$$Fe + Cu^{2+} + 2Cl^- \longrightarrow Fe^{2+} + 2Cl^- + Cu$$

The salt produced, ferrous chloride, is soluble and thus remains as separate ions in the solution.

(4) DOUBLE DECOMPOSITION (METATHESIS)

A reaction between two compounds to form two new compounds. Many examples of this type of reaction involve water solutions of salts. There is an exchange of ion partners:

in water $AgNO_3 + NaCl \longrightarrow AgCl + NaNO_3$

$$BaCl_2 + Na_2SO_4 \longrightarrow BaSO_4 + 2NaCl$$

Again the reactions are better represented by showing the separate ions of the salts with charges equal to their valence numbers.

$$Ag^+ + NO_3^- + Na^+ + Cl^- \longrightarrow AgCl + Na^+ + NO_3^-$$

and $\quad Ba^{2+} + 2Cl^- + 2Na^+ + SO_4^{2-} \longrightarrow BaSO_4 + 2Na^+ + 2Cl^-$

In the above equations, all compounds are water soluble except the $AgCl$ and the $BaSO_4$. These salts are deposited as insoluble solids (precipitates) from the solutions. Precipitates are indicated by a line drawn under the formula or by a downward pointing arrow written after the formula, $BaSO_4\downarrow$.

The insoluble products $AgCl$ and $BaSO_4$ may be written as Ag^+Cl^- and $Ba^{2+}SO_4^{2-}$ because they are compounds made of ions not molecules.

(5) NEUTRALIZATION

An acid reacts with a base to produce a salt and water.

$$HCl + KOH \longrightarrow KCl + H_2O$$

$$H_2SO_4 + Ca(OH)_2 \longrightarrow CaSO_4 + 2H_2O$$

Since acids in solution yield H^+ and bases provide OH^- neutralization is a reaction of H^+ ions of the acid with just enough OH^- of a base to form water molecules. No excess of H^+ or OH^- remains after neutralization. The salt produced is a compound of the positive ion of the base with the negative ion of the acid.

$$H^+ + Cl^- + K^+ + OH^- \longrightarrow K^+ + Cl^- + H_2O$$

$$2H^+ + SO_4^{2-} + Ca^{2+} + 2OH^- \longrightarrow CaSO_4 + 2H_2O$$

Note again that H^+ ions are shown in these equations where the hydrated hydrogen ion (hydronium ion) $H^+.H_2O$ or H_3O^+ should be used.

Instead of a base (metal hydroxide) reacting to neutralize an acid, a basic oxide (metal oxide) may also cause neutralization.

$$CaO + 2HNO_3 \longrightarrow Ca(NO_3)_2 + H_2O$$

Acidic oxides such as CO_2 and SO_3 react with bases to form salts and water to illustrate other examples of neutralization reactions.

$$CO_2 + Ca(OH)_2 \longrightarrow CaCO_3 + H_2O$$

$$SO_3 + 2KOH \longrightarrow K_2SO_4 + H_2O$$

Wider Classification of Reaction Type.

Instead of grouping reactions as decomposition, displacement, neutralization etc. two general classes may be used:

Oxidation - Reduction and Metathesis

Any reaction in which there is no change in valence number of any atom or no electrons are transferred between atoms is an example of metathesis.

Oxidation-reduction reactions are all other reactions in which electron transfer or valence number changes do occur. This topic is taken in chapter "**Oxidation-Reduction**", page 70.

III. RULES FOR SOLUBILITY OF COMPOUNDS IN WATER

(a) Nitrates, chlorates and acetates are soluble.

(b) Chlorides, iodides and bromides are soluble except Ag^+, Pb^{++} and Hg^+.

(c) Sulfates are soluble except Ba^{++}, Sr^{++} and Pb^{++}. $CaSO_4$ and Ag_2SO_4 are slightly soluble.

(d) Hydroxides are insoluble except those of the alkali metals and NH_4^+. The hydroxides of alkaline earths are sparingly soluble.

(e) Carbonates, phosphates are silicates are insoluble except those of the alkali metals and NH_4^+.

(f) Sulfides are insoluble except those of the alkali metals and NH_4^+. The sulfides of Mg^{++}, Al^{+++}, Cr^{+++} and the alkaline earth metals cannot be precipitated because they decompose.

IV. THE ELECTROMOTIVE (ACTIVITY) SERIES OF METALS

Facts About the Series

1. K — Potassium
2. Na — Sodium
3. Ba — Barium
4. Sr — Strontium
5. Ca — Calcium
6. Mg — Magnesium
7. Al — Aluminum
8. Mn — Manganese
9. Zn — Zinc
10. Cr — Chromium
11. Cd — Cadmium
12. Fe — Iron
13. Co — Cobalt
14. Ni — Nickel
15. Sn — Tin
16. Pb — Lead
17. HYDROGEN
18. Cu — Copper
19. Sb — Antimony
20. Hg — Mercury
21. Ag — Silver
22. Pt — Platinum
23. Au — Gold

(a) The metals are arranged in the order of decreasing activity.

Example

Potassium is more active than sodium, while sodium is more active than barium, etc.

(b) Each metal displaces each succeeding one from solution.

Example

$$Zn + CuSO_4 \longrightarrow Cu + ZnSO_4$$
(In solution)   (In solution)

The above reaction may be represented ionically:

$$Zn + Cu^{++} \longrightarrow Cu + Zn^{++}$$
(In solution)   (In solution)

Zn is above Cu in the Electromotive Series.

$$Fe + AlCl_3 \longrightarrow \text{No reaction}$$
(In solution)

Fe is below Al in the Electromotive Series.

(c) Metals 1 — 5 liberate hydrogen from cold water. Metal 6 displaces hydrogen from hot water.

EXAMPLE

$$Ca + 2H_2O \longrightarrow Ca(OH)_2 + H_2$$
Cold   Calcium hydroxide

$$Cu + H_2O \longrightarrow \text{No reaction}$$
Cold

(Note the positions of Cu and Ca in the Electromotive Series)

(d) Metals 1 — 12 liberate hydrogen from steam.

EXAMPLE

$$2Al + 3H_2O \longrightarrow Al_2O_3 + 3H_2$$
  Steam   Aluminum oxide

$$Pb + H_2O \longrightarrow \text{No reaction}$$
  Steam

(Note the positions of Al and Pb in the Electromotive Series)

(e) Metals 1 – 16 liberate hydrogen from acids.

EXAMPLES

$$Sn + H_2SO_4 \longrightarrow SnSO_4 + H_2$$
  Sulfuric   Stannous
  acid   sulfate

$$Hg + H_2SO_4 \longrightarrow \text{No reaction}$$

(Note the positions of Sn and Hg in the Electromotive Series)

(f) Metals from 1 – 20 combine with oxygen.

EXAMPLES

$$2Zn + O_2 \longrightarrow 2ZnO$$
                       Zinc oxide

$$Pt + O_2 \longrightarrow \text{No reaction}$$

(Note: Oxides of Ag, Pt and Au can be formed only by
  indirect methods.)

(g) Oxides of Metals 12 – 23 can be reduced by hydrogen; the other
  oxides cannot be reduced by hydrogen.

EXAMPLES

$$NiO + H_2 \longrightarrow Ni + H_2O$$
Nickel oxide

$$Al_2O_3 + H_2 \longrightarrow \text{No reaction}$$

(Note the positions of Ni and Al in the Electromotive Series.)

(h) Oxides of metals 20 – 23 can be decomposed by the heat of a
  bunsen burner; the other oxides cannot be reduced by the heat
  of a bunsen burner.

EXAMPLES

$$2Au_2O_3 + heat \longrightarrow 4Au + 3O_2$$
Auric oxide

$$Al_2O_3 \quad + heat \longrightarrow \text{No reaction}$$

(Note the positions of Au and Al in the Electromotive Series.)

(i) It is to be noted that the most active elements form the most stable compounds.

EXAMPLES

$$2Ag_2O \quad + heat \longrightarrow 4Ag + O_2$$

$$CaO \quad + heat \longrightarrow \text{No reaction}$$

(Note: Ca is more active than Ag. Calcium oxide is more stable than silver oxide.)

V. CHEMICAL PROPERTIES OF METALLIC COMPOUNDS

ACTION OF HEAT

(a) On Hydroxides

All hydroxides lose water when heated to form the oxide with the exception of the alkali metal hydroxides:

$$2Al(OH)_3 \xrightarrow{\text{heat}} Al_2O_3 + 3H_2O$$

$$KOH \xrightarrow{\text{heat}} \text{No reaction}$$

The hydroxides of mercury and silver are not stable; they decompose to form the oxide and water:

$$AgNO_3 + NaOH \longrightarrow NaNO_3 + AgOH$$
$$\text{Not Stable}$$

$$2AgOH \longrightarrow Ag_2O + H_2O$$

(b) On Carbonates

All carbonates lose carbon dioxide when heated to form the oxide with the exception of the alkali metal carbonates:

$$ZnCO_3 \xrightarrow{\text{heat}} ZnO + CO_2$$

$$Na_2CO_3 \xrightarrow{\text{heat}} \text{No reaction}$$

The carbonates of aluminum and tin do not exist because the hydroxides of these elements are not basic enough to form the carbonates.

(c) On Nitrates

The nitrates of the alkali metals yield nitrites and oxygen on heating. The nitrates of all other metals yield nitrogen dioxide, oxygen and the metallic oxide on heating:

$$2KNO_3 \xrightarrow{\text{heat}} 2KNO_2 + O_2$$

$$2Pb(NO_3)_2 \xrightarrow{\text{heat}} 2PbO + 4NO_2 + O_2$$

(d) On Sulfates

The sulfates of all metals decompose to sulfur trioxide and the metallic oxide on heating, except the alkali metal and alkaline earth sulfates:

$$Al_2(SO_4)_3 \xrightarrow{\text{heat}} Al_2O_3 + 3SO_3$$

$$Na_2SO_4 \xrightarrow{\text{heat}} \text{No reaction}$$

$$BaSO_4 \xrightarrow{\text{heat}} \text{No reaction}$$

The hydroxides, carbonates, nitrates and the sulfates of the metals below copper in the electromotive series yield the metal upon heating, since the oxides of these metals decompose on heating.

$$2Au(OH)_3 \xrightarrow{\text{heat}} Au_2O_3 + 3H_2O$$

But Au_2O_3 is decomposed by heat:

$$2Au_2O_3 \xrightarrow{\text{heat}} 4Au + 3O_2$$

The overall reaction may be written:

$$4Au(OH)_3 \xrightarrow{\text{heat}} 4Au + 6H_2O + 3O_2$$

$$Ag_2CO_3 \xrightarrow{\text{heat}} Ag_2O + CO_2$$

But Ag_2O is decomposed by heat:

$$2Ag_2O \xrightarrow{\text{heat}} 4Ag + O_2$$

The overall reaction may be written:

$$2Ag_2CO_3 \xrightarrow{\text{heat}} 4Ag + 2CO_2 + O_2$$

PROBLEMS

(ANSWERS ON PAGE 153)

1. Complete and balance:

(a) $Na + Br_2$

(b) $K + I_2$

(c) $Ca + O_2$

(d) $Ba + Cl_2$

(e) $H_2 + Br_2$

(f) $Al + Br_2$

(g) $Zn + Cl_2$

(h) $CaO + SO_2$

(i) $K_2O + SO_3$

(j) $Cu + Cl_2$

2. Complete and balance:

(a) $NaClO_3 + heat$

(b) $KNO_3 + heat$

(c) $MgCO_3 + heat$

(d) $NaNO_3 + heat$

(e) $BaO_2 + heat$

(f) $Ag_2O + heat$

3. Complete and balance. If no reaction takes place indicate by N.R.

(a) $Cd + HCl$

(b) $Cr + H_2SO_4$

(c) $Ag + H_2SO_4$

(d) $Zn + H_3PO_4$

(e) $Zn + Pt(SO_4)_2$

(f) $Cr + HgCl_2$

(g) $Hg + Fe(NO_3)_3$

(h) $Fe + SnSO_4$

4. Complete and balance:

(a) $AgNO_3 + Na_2CrO_4$

(b) $BaCl_2 + Na_2CO_3$

(c) $CuSO_4 + H_2S$

(d) $ZnCl_2 + H_2S$

(e) $AgNO_3 + H_3PO_4$

(f) $Pb(NO_3)_2 + HCl$

(g) $AsCl_3 + H_2S$

(h) $MnCl_2 + H_2S$

5. Complete and balance. If no reaction takes place indicate by N.R.

(a) $K + H_2O$

(b) $Sr + H_2O$

(c) $Zn + steam$

(d) $Cd + steam$

(e) $Al + HCl$

(f) $Pt + H_2SO_4$

(g) $Mg + HgSO_4$

(h) $Zn + FeSO_4$

(i) $Fe + AgNO_3$

(j) $Au_2O_3 + heat$

(k) $Al_2O_3 + heat$

(l) $Ag_2O + heat$

6. Complete and balance. If no reaction takes place indicate by N.R.

(a) $Fe(OH)_3 + heat$

(b) $Zn(OH)_2 + heat$

(f) $Hg(NO_3) + heat$

(g) $Fe(NO_3)_3 + heat$

(c) KOH + heat	(h) $CaSO_4$ + heat
(d) Na_2CO_3 + heat	(i) K_2SO_4 + heat
(e) $CaCO_3$ + heat	(j) $HgCO_3$ + heat

WEIGHT RELATIONS IN CHEMICAL REACTIONS

I. USING EQUATIONS IN CALCULATIONS

Any balanced chemical equation may be used to give different kinds of information about the reaction represented.

$$2H_2 + O_2 \longrightarrow 2H_2O$$

(1) Hydrogen combines chemically with oxygen to form water.

(2) Every two molecules of hydrogen require one molecule of oxygen and two water molecules are produced.

(3) In terms of moles, $2 \times 6.03 \times 10^{23}$ hydrogen molecules react with $1 \times 6.03 \times 10^{23}$ oxygen molecules to produce $2 \times 6.03 \times 10^{23}$ water molecules. Since 6.03×10^{23} molecules = 1 mole, it follows that 2 moles of hydrogen react with 1 mole of oxygen to produce 2 moles of water.

(4) The weight of 1 mole of a pure substance is the quantity represented by the Gram Formula Weight (Gram Molecular Weight). Therefore, 2×2 g hydrogen react with 1×32 g oxygen to form 2×18 g water.

Many weight to weight calculations from equations can be solved by relating the numbers of moles in the balanced equation to the actual weights of the reactants or products used in stating the problem.

EXAMPLES

1. How many grams of hydrogen will react with 4.0 g of oxygen to form water? Atomic Weights H = 1, O = 16

$$\underset{\text{2 moles}}{2H_2} + \underset{\text{1 mole}}{O_2} \longrightarrow \underset{\text{2 moles}}{2H_2O}$$

Oxygen, O_2 1 mole = 32 g Then 4 g = $\frac{4}{32}$ mole

1 mole O_2 reacts with 2 moles H_2

$\frac{4}{32}$ moles O_2 react with $\frac{4}{32} \times 2$ moles $H_2 = \frac{4}{32} \times 2 \times 2$ g hydrogen

2. How many grams of silver nitrate will react with 2.925 g of sodium chloride? Atom Weights Ag = 108, N = 14, O = 16, Cl = 35.5
First, the balanced equation

$$\begin{array}{ccc} ? \text{ g} & 2.925 \text{ g} & \\ AgNO_3 & + \quad NaCl & \longrightarrow \quad AgCl \; + \; NaNO_3 \\ 1 \text{ mole} & 1 \text{ mole} & \end{array}$$

NaCl, 1 mole = 23 + 35.5 = 58.5 g Then 2.925 g = $\frac{2.925}{58.5}$ mole

$AgNO_3$, 1 mole = 108 + 14 + (3 × 16) = 170 g

Since 1 mole NaCl reacts with 1 mole $AgNO_3$

$\frac{2.925}{58.5}$ mole NaCl reacts with $\frac{2.925}{58.5}$ mole $AgNO_3$

$$\frac{2.925}{58.5} \times 170 = 8.5 \text{ g } AgNO_3$$

Note that the problem does not ask for weights of products. Therefore, there is no need to use the right hand side of the equation.

3. What is the weight of (a) oxygen (b) potassium chloride formed by the decomposition of 7.35 g of potassium chlorate?

$$\begin{array}{cc} 2KClO_3 \longrightarrow & 2KCl \; + \; 3O_2 \\ 2 \text{ moles} & 2 \text{ moles} \quad 3 \text{ moles} \end{array}$$

Atomic Weights K = 39, Cl = 35.5, O = 16

Take each part of the problem separately.

(a) $KClO_3$ 1 mole = 39 + 35.5 + (3 × 16) = 122.5 g

O_2 1 mole = 2 × 16 = 32 g

7.35 g $KClO_3$ = $\frac{7.35}{122.5}$ mole

2 moles $KClO_3$ produce 3 moles O_2

1 mole $KClO_3$ produces $\frac{3}{2}$ moles O_2

and $\frac{7.35}{122.5}$ moles produces $\frac{7.35}{122.5} \times \frac{3}{2}$ moles O_2

$$\frac{7.35}{122.5} \times \frac{3}{2} \times 32 \text{ g of } O_2 = 2.4 \text{ g } O_2$$

56

(b) KCl, 1 mole = 74.5 g

2 moles KClO₃ produce 2 moles KCl

$\frac{7.35}{122.5}$ moles KClO₃ produces $\frac{7.35}{122.5}$ moles KCl

$\frac{7.35}{122.5} \times 74.5 = 4.95$ g KCl

4. How many ml of 45% H_2SO_4 solution are required to neutralize 250 ml of 12% NaOH solution? (Specific gravity of 45% H_2SO_4 solution is 1.34 and of 12% NaOH solution is 1.13.)

First, the balanced equation

$$H_2SO_4 + 2NaOH \longrightarrow Na_2SO_4 + 2H_2O$$
1 mole   2 moles

250 ml of 12% NaOH solution weighs 250 × 1.13 g and contains

$\frac{12}{100} \times 250 \times 1.13$ g of NaOH = 33.90 g

1 mole of NaOH is 40 g $\frac{33.90 \text{ g}}{40 \text{ g}}$ = 0.85 mole

From the equation, 0.5 moles of H_2SO_4 react with 1 mole of NaOH

Then 0.5 × 0.85 = 0.43 moles H_2SO_4 react with 0.85 moles NaOH

1 mole of H_2SO_4 weighs 98 g

0.43 moles weigh 0.43 × 98 = 42.2 g

1 ml of the 45% H_2SO_4 solution weighs 1.34 g and contains

0.45 × 1.34 g of hydrogen sulfate = 0.603 g

0.603 g hydrogen sulfate in 1 ml of H_2SO_4 solution

42.2 g hydrogen sulfate in $\frac{42.2}{0.603}$ = 70.0 ml H_2SO_4 solution.

PROBLEMS
(ANSWERS ON PAGE 154)

1. How many grams of calcium carbonate must be decomposed to obtain 28 g of calcium oxide,

$$CaCO_3 \longrightarrow CaO + CO_2$$

2. What weight of oxygen will combine with 64 g of sulfur?

$$S + O_2 \longrightarrow SO_2$$

3. How many grams of hydrogen chloride are obtained from 0.4 g of hydrogen?

$$H_2 + Cl_2 \longrightarrow 2HCl$$

4. How many grams of water are needed to combine with 112 g of calcium oxide?

$$CaO + H_2O \longrightarrow Ca(OH)_2$$

5. What weight of (a) oxygen (b) mercury will be obtained by the thermal decomposition of 315 g of mercury (II) oxide?

$$2HgO \longrightarrow 2Hg + O_2$$

6. How many grams of silver oxide must be heated to obtain 224 g of silver?

$$2Ag_2O \longrightarrow 4Ag + O_2$$

7. How many grams of iron are formed when 191 g of magnetic iron oxide are reduced by hydrogen?

$$Fe_3O_4 + 4H_2 \longrightarrow 3Fe + 4H_2O$$

8. Calculate the weight of (a) sodium chloride (b) silver nitrate required to precipitate 2.86 g of silver chloride.

$$NaCl + AgNO_3 \longrightarrow AgCl + NaNO_3$$

9. Calculate the volume of concentrated sulfuric acid solution required to react with 200 g of 80% sodium hydroxide. (The specific gravity of concentrated sulfuric acid solution is 1.85 and it contains 95% of sulfuric acid by weight.)

10. Calculate the volume of 20% hydrochloric acid solution required to react with 500 g of limestone (90% $CaCO_3$). (The specific gravity of 20% hydrochloric acid solution is 1.11).

$$CaCO_3 + 2HCl \longrightarrow CaCl_2 + H_2O + CO_2$$

THE GRAM MOLECULAR VOLUME

I. A MOLE OF A GAS

One mole of any gas such as hydrogen H_2, oxygen O_2, ammonia NH_3, acetylene C_2H_2 etc. contains 6.02×10^{23} molecules of the gas.

Another common relationship applies to all gases. 1 mole of any gas at STP occupies a volume of 22.4 liters. The volume 22.4 liters is called the gram molecular volume or GMV.

Examples: Each of these statements concerns the same quantity of oxygen.

1 mole of O_2 is 32 g or 6.02×10^{23} O_2 molecules or 22.4 liters of oxygen at STP.

Similarly, 1 mole of ammonia NH_3 is (14 + 3) g or 6.02×10^{23} molecules or 22.4 liters of ammonia at STP.

The gram molecular volume relationship for all gases follows from Avogadro's law: equal volumes of all gases at the same temperature and pressure contain the same number of molecules. The converse is also true; equal numbers of molecules of gases will occupy the same volume, if the temperature and pressure is constant.

Note that 1 mole of any gas represents the same number of molecules and the same volume (22.4 liters at STP) but the weight of 1 mole of a gas is determined by its own gram molecular weight.

II. DENSITY OF A GAS CALCULATED FROM GRAM MOLECULAR VOLUME

If the formula for a gas is known and the atomic weights, the density in grams per liter at STP is readily calculated.

The general gas law may then be used to find the weight of any volume of the gas at other temperature and pressure conditions.

EXAMPLES

1. What is the density of carbon dioxide gas in grams per liter at STP? Atomic Weights C = 12, O = 16

Carbon dioxide, CO_2 1 mole = 12 + (2 × 16) = 44 g

1 mole of gas at STP is 22.4 liters in volume

$$\text{Density} = \frac{\text{Mass}}{\text{Volume}} = \frac{44 \text{ g}}{22.4 \text{ liters}} = 1.96 \text{ g per l.}$$

2. What is the weight of 200 ml of ammonia at STP?
   Atomic Weights   N = 14,   H = 1

   Ammonia NH_3 1 mole = 17 g weight, and has a volume 22.4 1.
   at STP.

      200 ml = 0.2 liter

   If 22.4 liters of gas weighs 17 g

      1 liter weighs $\dfrac{17}{22.4}$ g

      0.2 liter weighs $\dfrac{0.2 \times 17}{22.4}$ = 0.15 g

3. What is the weight of 4.7 liters of oxygen at 800 mm pressure
   and 25°C?   Atomic Weight O = 16

   (a) Since the weight of 22.4 liters of oxygen at STP (32 g) is
       known from the formula O_2, convert the gas volume given in
       the problem to STP.

       new volume (STP) = original volume × pressure factor ×
       temperature factor

       new volume = $4.7 \times \dfrac{800}{760} \times \dfrac{273}{295}$ liters

                   = 4.5 liters

   (b) At STP 22.4 liters of oxygen weigh 32 g

           4.5 liters weigh $\dfrac{4.5 \times 32}{22.4}$ = 2.2 g

       Then 4.7 1. at 800 mm and 25°C weighs 2.2 g

III. CALCULATING GRAM MOLECULAR WEIGHT FROM DENSITY

The density of a gas is a statement of a mass of a certain volume.
The gram molecular weight of the gas is found by calculating the
weight of 22.4 liters of the gas at STP.

EXAMPLES

1. What is the gram molecular weight of a gas if its density is
   2.5 g per liter at STP?

   At STP, 1 liter of the gas weighs 2.5 g

   Then, 22.4 1. at STP weigh 22.4 × 2.5 = 56.0 g

This is the weight of 1 mole of the gas and therefore the gram molecular weight is 56 g

2. At STP, 1400 ml of a gas weighs 2.1 g. Calculate the gram molecular weight of the gas.

At STP 1400 ml of the gas weighs 2.1 g

$$1 \text{ ml of the gas weighs } \frac{2.1}{1400} \text{ g}$$

$$1 \text{ mole (22.4 1.) or 22400 ml weigh } 22400 \times \frac{2.1}{1400} \text{ g}$$

the gram molecular weight is 33.6 g

3. Calculate the weight of 1 mole of a gas if 245 ml at 45°C and 658 mm pressure weighs 0.9 g.

(a) Convert the gas volume to standard conditions.

volume at STP = original volume × pressure factor × temperature factor

$$\text{new volume} = 245 \times \frac{273}{318} \times \frac{658}{760} = 178 \text{ ml}$$

(b) 178 ml of gas at STP weighs 0.9 g

The volume of gas has changed but not the number of molecules or the mass.

178 ml = 0.178 1. of gas at STP weighs 0.9 g

$$1 \text{ liter weighs } \frac{0.9}{0.178} \text{ g}$$

$$22.4 \text{ liters weigh } 22.4 \times \frac{0.9}{0.178} = 113 \text{ g}$$

1 mole of the gas weighs 113 g

IV. CALCULATIONS OF VOLUMES AND WEIGHTS IN EQUATIONS

In a problem asking the volume of a gaseous reactant or product to be calculated knowing the weight of some other reactant or product, the relationship 1 mole of any gas = 22.4 liters at STP is used.

EXAMPLES

1. What volume of hydrogen measured at STP is obtained by the reaction of 3.66 g of magnesium with sulfuric acid?

Note: assume there is sufficient acid present to use up all of the magnesium.   Atomic Weight Mg = 24.4

$$Mg + H_2SO_4 \longrightarrow MgSO_4 + H_2$$
$$1 \text{ mole} \qquad\qquad\qquad\qquad 1 \text{ mole}$$

1 mole of magnesium = its gram atomic weight = 24.4 g

1 mole of H_2 gas has a volume of 22.4 liters at STP

$$3.66 \text{ g Mg is } \frac{3.66}{24.4} = \frac{3}{20} \text{ mole}$$

Since 1 mole Mg yields 1 mole H_2

$$\frac{3}{20} \text{ mole of Mg yields } \frac{3}{20} \text{ mole } H_2 \text{ or } \frac{3}{20} \times 22.4 \text{ liters}$$

$$= 3.34 \text{ l. at STP}$$

2. What volume of hydrogen sulfide at STP is required to precipitate 3.6 g of copper (II) sulfide from a solution of copper (II) sulfate? Atomic Weights Cu = 63.5, S = 32

$$CuSO_4 + H_2S \longrightarrow CuS + H_2SO_4$$
$$1 \text{ mole} \qquad\qquad\qquad 1 \text{ mole}$$

Copper (II) sulfide, CuS 1 mole is 95.5 g

$$3.6 \text{ g CuS is } \frac{3.6}{95.5} \text{ mole}$$

1 mole of CuS is obtained using 1 mole of H_2S

then, $\dfrac{3.6}{95.5}$ mole of CuS requires $\dfrac{3.6}{95.5}$ mole of H_2S

1 mole of H_2S at STP is 22.4 liters

$$\frac{3.6}{95.5} \text{ mole of } H_2S \text{ is } \frac{3.6 \times 22.4}{95.5} = 0.85 \text{ liters}$$

PROBLEMS

(ANSWERS ON PAGE 154)

1. The density of a gas is 1.374 $\frac{g}{\ell}$ at STP. Calculate the molecular weight of the gas.

2. If 200 ml of gas weigh 9.55 g at STP, calculate the molecular weight.

3. If 300 ml of a gas weigh 9.5 g at 27° C and 740 mm, calculate the molecular weight.

62

4. A mass of 1.25 g of liquid was vaporized giving 600 ml of vapor collected over water at 30°C and 760 mm. Calculate the molecular weight.

5. Calculate the weight of 1 liter at STP of (a) CH_4, (b) H_2S, (c) Cl_2, (d) C_2H_6, (e) O_2.

6. Calculate the density in $\frac{g}{l}$ at STP of (a) N_2, (b) He, (c) Ar, (d) SiF_4, (e) CO_2.

7. How many liters of O_2 at STP are formed by heating 40 g of KNO_3?

8. How many liters of O_2 at STP are formed by heating 36 g of $KClO_3$?

9. How many liters of O_2 at 27°C and 770 mm are formed by heating 50 g of BaO_2?

10. How many liters of H_2 at 20°C and 765 mm are necessary to reduce 120 g of Fe_3O_4?

11. What weight of Al must be treated with acid to form 450 ml of H_2 at STP?

12. What weight of $KClO_3$ must be heated to obtain 3.2 liters of O_2 at 27°C and 745 mm?

13. What volume will 98 g of O_2 occupy at 30°C and 745 mm pressure?

14. What volume will 200 g of NH_3 occupy at 27°C and 780 mm pressure?

15. Calculate the weight of 250 ml of CO_2 at 40°C and 4 atm.

16. When an impure sample of Al weighing 0.5 g was treated with excess HCl, 480 ml of H_2 at 20°C and 765 mm were obtained. Calculate the percent purity of the Al.

17. A hydrocarbon is composed of 92.3% C and 7.7% H. Upon vaporizing 0.695 g of the hydrocarbon, 273 ml of vapor were formed at 100°C and 760 mm. Calculate the molecular formula of this hydrocarbon.

18. A gaseous hydrocarbon is composed of 80% C and 20% H. At STP 500 ml of this gas was found to weigh 0.67 g. Calculate the molecular formula of this compound.

REACTIONS OF GASES

I. VOLUME – VOLUME RELATIONSHIPS

In any chemical reaction which has gases reacting or gases produced the relative volumes of gases are found by inspecting the balanced equation. There is no need to use atomic weights or molecular weights, and the actual temperature and pressure conditions of the reaction do not have to be stated. Constant temperature and pressure are assumed for all gas volumes measured.

EXAMPLE I.   What volume of hydrogen will react with 300 ml of chlorine and what volume of hydrogen chloride gas is produced?

Note that the temperature and pressure conditions are assumed to be the same for all gas volumes being measured.

$$H_2 + Cl_2 \longrightarrow 2HCl$$
$$\text{1 mole}\quad \text{1 mole} \qquad\qquad \text{2 moles}$$

The substances are in the proportion of 1 : 1 : 2 by moles. At the constant temperature and pressure conditions of STP, 1 mole of any gas occupies 22.4 litres. It follows that at STP, these gases are in the proportion of 22.4 : 22.4 : 44.8 by volume. Now if we allow the gases to react at some other temperature and pressure, but with the same conditions for each gas, the gas volumes are still in the proportion of 1 : 1 : 2. In going from STP to some other temperature and pressure the general gas law would apply to the volumes of hydrogen, chlorine and hydrogen chloride as a constant factor so that the relative gas volumes would remain in the ratio 1 : 1 : 2.

Therefore, 300 ml chlorine combines with 300 ml hydrogen to form 600 ml of hydrogen chloride.

EXAMPLE 2.   Calculate the volumes of hydrogen and oxygen required to produce 8 liters of steam.

Note that if steam is to be a product and not water, the temperature and pressure conditions must be such that gaseous steam exists but not liquid water. Again, consider all volumes as measured at the same temperature and pressure conditions.

	$2H_2$	+	O_2	$\longrightarrow$	$2H_2O$
mole ratio	2	:	1	:	2
volume ratio	2	:	1	:	2
therefore	8 liters	:	4 liters	:	8 liters

64

EXAMPLE 3. What volume of oxygen is required for the complete combustion of 80 ml of ethane gas, and what volume of carbon dioxide is produced?

First, the balanced equation:

$$2C_2H_6 \quad + \quad 7O_2 \longrightarrow 4CO_2 \quad + \quad 6H_2O$$

mole ratio	2	: 7	:	4
volume ratio	2	: 7	:	4

$$80 \text{ ml} \quad : \quad \frac{7}{2} \times 80 \text{ ml} : \quad 2 \times 80 \text{ ml}$$

or   80 ml   :   280 ml   :   160 ml

In some cases a gaseous reactant may be present in excess amount. Then the actual excess quantity will remain mixed with any gaseous products.

EXAMPLE 4. What is the volume composition of the gases remaining after 25 ml of methane is exploded with 75 ml of oxygen? The gas volumes are measured at $27°C$ and 748 mm pressure.

$$CH_4 \quad + \quad 2O_2 \longrightarrow CO_2 \quad + \quad 2H_2O$$

mole ratio	1	:	2	:	1	: 2
volume ratio	1	:	2	:	1	

At $27°C$ and 748 mm pressure H_2O exists as liquid, and is omitted from the volume ratio.

In a mixture of 25 ml of methane and 75 ml of oxygen, the oxygen is present in excess amount. The volume ratio shows that 25 ml methane reacts with 50 ml of oxygen to form 25 ml of carbon dioxide.

Therefore, the volume composition of the gaseous mixture produced is 25 ml carbon dioxide and $75 - 50 = 25$ ml of excess oxygen.

Note that in solving volume − volume relationships from balanced equations i) the mole ratio is the same as ratio of molecules in the balanced equation and
ii) the volume ratio for gases only is the same as the ratio of molecules in the equation also.

EXAMPLE 5. To a 50 ml sample of a mixture of nitrogen and hydrogen were added 10 ml of oxygen and the mixture was exploded. After removal of the water vapor, the volume of the remaining gases measured 45 ml. Assuming no reaction between N_2 and H_2 and between N_2 and O_2, calculate the percentage composition of the original mixture.

50 ml original sample + 10 ml O_2 = 60 ml total volume
60 ml total volume - 45 ml residual gases = 15 ml decrease
in volume

The reaction is:

$$2H_2 + O_2 \longrightarrow 2H_2O \text{ (removed)}$$

2 volumes of H_2 + 1 volume of O_2 yield zero volume or,

3 volumes $\longrightarrow$ 0 Volume, since the H_2O is removed

$\frac{2}{3}$ of decrease in volume = volume of H_2

$\frac{1}{3}$ of decrease in volume = volume of O_2

Therefore

$$\frac{2}{3} \times 15 \text{ ml} = 10 \text{ ml } H_2$$

In the original mixture then:

$$\frac{10 \text{ ml } H_2}{50 \text{ ml } H_2 + N_2} + 100 = 20\% \text{ } H_2$$

Remainder must be N_2 or 80% N_2.

PROBLEMS

(ANSWERS ON PAGE 154)

1. What volume of H_2 is necessary to prepare 40 ml of HCl by the combination of H_2 and Cl_2?

2. The equation for the oxidation of nitric oxide is

$$2NO + O_2 \longrightarrow 2NO_2$$

How many ml of NO and O_2 are necessary to form 60 ml of NO_2?

3. (a) How many liters of CO_2 are formed when 3.5 liters of CO are burned? (b) How many liters of O_2 are required?

4. How many liters of CO_2 and steam are formed when 1500 ml of C_2H_6 are burned?

$$2C_2H_6 + 7O_2 \longrightarrow 4CO_2 + 6H_2O$$

5. How many ml of propane C_3H_8 must be burned to form 30 ml of CO_2 and what volume of O_2 will be necessary?

6. How many liters of N_2 and H_2 are necessary to form 30 liters of NH_3 in the Haber process?

$$N_2 + 3H_2 \longrightarrow 2NH_3$$

7. What volume of O_2 is necessary for the complete combustion of 60 ml of H_2S?

$$2H_2S + 3O_2 \longrightarrow 2H_2O + 2SO_2$$

8. A mixture of 40 ml of propane and 300 ml of oxygen is exploded. What is the volume composition of the remaining gases if the volumes are measured at STP?

9. Nitric oxide is prepared commercially by the oxidation of NH_3. How many ml of NH_3 and O_2 are required to form 200 ml of NO?

$$4NH_3 + 5O_2 \longrightarrow 4NO + 6H_2O$$

10. How many liters of air are necessary to burn 25 liters of CH_4 to CO_2 and H_2O, (Air contains approximately 20% O_2 by volume.)

11. How many liters of air are necessary to burn 50 liters of water gas which is composed of equal quantities CO and H_2 by volume?

12. To a 100 ml sample of a mixture of nitrogen and oxygen were added 50 ml of hydrogen and the mixture was exploded. After removal of the water vapor, the volume of the remaining gases measured 110 ml. Calculate the composition of the original mixture. (Assume that nitrogen does not react with hydrogen nor oxygen.)

EQUIVALENT WEIGHT
I. EQUIVALENT WEIGHT

The equivalent weight of an element is the weight which will react with 8 g of oxygen or 1 g of hydrogen or with the equivalent weight of any other element.

Thus since 9 g of aluminum will combine with 8 g of oxygen, the equivalent weight of aluminum is 9. Aluminum has a gram equivalent weight of 9 g. It follows that if 9 g of aluminum is reacted with excess acid to liberate hydrogen, the gram equivalent weight of hydrogen (1 g) will be liberated by the gram equivalent weight of aluminum (9 g).

Pure substances, elements or compounds, react in the proportion of their equivalent weights.

EXAMPLES

1. What is the gram equivalent weight of a metal if 3.0 g combines with 1.2 g of oxygen?

$$1.2 \text{ g oxygen reacts with } 3.0 \text{ metal}$$

$$1 \text{ g oxygen reacts with } \frac{3.0}{1.2} \text{ g metal}$$

$$8 \text{ g oxygen reacts with } \frac{8 \times 3.0}{1.2}$$

$$= 20 \text{ g metal}$$

The gram equivalent weight is 20 g.

2. The oxide of an element is 40% by weight oxygen. Calculate the equivalent weight of the element.

40% oxygen in the oxide, therefore $100 - 40 = 60\%$ element

$$40 \text{ g oxygen reacts with } 60 \text{ g element}$$

$$1 \text{ g oxygen reacts with } \frac{60}{40} \text{ g element}$$

$$8 \text{ g oxygen reacts with } \frac{8 \times 60}{40} \text{ g element}$$

$$= 12 \text{ g}$$

The equivalent weight of the element is 12.

3. Calculate the gram equivalent of a metal if 0.26 g of hydrogen is released from an acid by 2.34 g of the metal.

$$0.26 \text{ g hydrogen displaced by } 2.34 \text{ g metal}$$

$$1 \text{ g hydrogen is displaced by } \frac{2.34}{0.26} \text{ g metal}$$

$$= 9.0 \text{ g}$$

Gram equivalent of the metal is 9 g.

4. What weight of a metal reacts with 0.6 g of chlorine? The equivalent weight of chlorine is 35.5, and the equivalent of the metal is 23.

Substances react in the proportion of their equivalent weights.

35.5 g chlorine react with 23 g metal

1 g chlorine react with $\dfrac{23}{35.5}$ g metal

0.6 g chlorine react with $\dfrac{0.6 \times 23}{35.5}$

$= 0.39$ g metal

5. When 0.5 g of a metal were treated with excess acid, 190 ml of hydrogen at STP were liberated. Calculate the equivalent weight of the metal.

1 mole of hydrogen, H_2 is 2 g or 22.4 liters at STP. Since the gram equivalent of hydrogen is 1g it follows that 11.2 liters of hydrogen at STP is also the equivalent of hydrogen.

190 ml $= 0.19$ liters

0.19 liters hydrogen liberated by 0.5 g metal

1 liter hydrogen liberated by $\dfrac{0.5}{0.19}$ g metal

11.2 liters liberated by $\dfrac{11.2 \times 0.5}{0.19} = 29.9$ g metal

The equivalent of the metal is 29.9

If the volume of hydrogen is measured at a different temperature and pressure, the gas laws are applied to convert the volume to STP. Then the problem is solved as in example 5.

6. When 0.75 g of a metal was treated with excess acid, 500 ml of H_2 at 20°C and 380 mm pressure were displaced. Calculate the equivalent weight of the metal.

It is first necessary to convert the volume of H_2 liberated to STP.

$$500 \times \dfrac{273}{293} \times \dfrac{380}{760} = 233 \text{ ml } H_2 \text{ at STP}$$

233 ml of $H_2 = 0.233$ liters of H_2

Since 0.233 liters of H_2 is displaced by 0.75 g of the metal

then 11.2 liters of H_2 will be displaced by $\dfrac{0.75}{0.233} \times 11.2 = 36$ g

The equivalent weight of the metal is 36.

PROBLEMS

(ANSWERS ON PAGE 154)

1. Two grams of a metal displace 0.05 g of H_2. Calculate the equivalent weight of the metal.

2. Forty-six grams of a metal displace 2.0 g of H_2. Calculate the equivalent weight of the metal.

3. It was found that 1.2 g of a metal combine with 0.1 g of O_2. Calculate the equivalent weight of the metal.

4. Calculate the equivalent weight of the metal: (a) When 3 g of an oxide were reduced, 2.8 g of a metal were formed. (b) An oxide of a metal contains 16% oxygen.

5. When 2.5 g of a metal were treated with excess acid, 2.8 liters of H_2 at STP were liberated. Calculate the equivalent weight of the metal.

6. When 5.0 g of an element are treated with excess acid, 8 liters of H_2 at STP were liberated. Calculate the equivalent weight of the metal.

7. When 1.67 g of a metal were treated with sulfuric acid, 2170 ml of H_2 at 770 mm pressure and 15°C were liberated. Calculate the equivalent weight of the metal.

8. When 0.82 g of a metal was treated with acid, 208 ml of H_2 at 765 mm pressure and 20°C were liberated. Calculate the equivalent weight of the metal.

9. Analysis shows that 8.1 g of an oxide contain 5.66 g of iron. Calculate the equivalent weight of the iron.

10. The equivalent weight of chlorine is 35.5 g. It was found that 2.16 g of an element combine with chlorine, to form 2.8 g of a compound. Calculate the equivalent weight of the element.

OXIDATION-REDUCTION

I. MEANINGS OF OXIDATION AND REDUCTION

Oxidation occurs when a substance loses electrons in a chemical reaction. The lost electrons must be gained by some other substance which is said to be reduced. For example, copper reacts with sulfur to form copper (II) sulfide. Neutral copper atoms represented Cu^o each give up 2 electrons to neutral sulfur atoms represented S^o.

$$Cu^o + S^o \longrightarrow Cu^{2+}S^{2-}$$

Copper, the substance oxidized, loses electrons.

Sulfur, the substance reduced, gains electrons.

The reaction is classed as a reduction-oxidation or redox, because if one reactant is oxidized by loss of electrons, another reactant is reduced as it gains electrons.

Neutral atoms and charged ions are assigned valence numbers or oxidation numbers. Oxidation is also defined as an increase in positive oxidation number. Reduction is a decrease in positive oxidation number, or an increase in negative oxidation number. For example:-

$$2FeCl_2 + Cl_2 \longrightarrow 2FeCl_3$$

The iron in $FeCl_2$ has an oxidation number of +2, and in $FeCl_3$ the oxidation number of the Fe is +3. Therefore the substance oxidized is the iron of the $FeCl_2$ because its oxidation number has a positive increase from +2 to +3. The substance reduced is the chlorine of the chlorine molecule Cl_2 which has an oxidation number of zero. It changes to chloride ion Cl^- in the $FeCl_3$ with an oxidation number of -1. The change in negative oxidation number from zero to -1 indicates reduction.

II. OXIDATION NUMBERS IN FORMULAS

Some general rules apply in determining an unknown oxidation number in a formula.

1. Oxygen has oxidation number -2 except in peroxides where it is -1.

2. Hydrogen has oxidation number +1 except in hydrides where it is -1.

3. The oxidation number of an element not combined with other elements is zero.

Each element in these examples has zero oxidation number:

Na, Al, O_2, H_2, P_4.

4. Any simple ion, Na^+, Mg^{2+}, Cl^-, S^{2-} etc., has oxidation number equal to the charge on the ion.

5. The sum of all the positive and negative oxidation numbers in an ion equals the charge on the ion, and is the total oxidation number for that ion.

NH_4^+ has total oxidation number +1

HCO_3^- has total oxidation number -1

SO_4^{2-} has total oxidation number -2

6. The total oxidation number in a molecule is zero. This means that the sum of all the positive and negative oxidation numbers of the atoms in the formula is zero.

H_2SO_4, KNO_3, $(NH_4)_2CO_3$, NaH_2PO_4 all have total oxidation number zero.

EXAMPLES

1. What is the oxidation number of sulfur in $CaSO_4$?

Ca has oxidation number +2, its valence number.

O has oxidation number -2, its valence number.

The total negative oxidation number is $4 \times (-2) = -8$

1 Ca atom with 4 O atoms totals $+2 + (-8) = -6$

If the total oxidation number for the formula is zero, the S must have an oxidation number +6.

2. What is the oxidation number of Cr in $K_2Cr_2O_7$?

2 K is $2 \times (+1) = +2$ 7 O is $7 \times (-2) = -14$

2 K with 7 O gives a value $+2 + (-14) = -12$

2 Cr must have oxidation number +12 to give the total oxidation number of zero for the formula

Cr has oxidation number +6

72

3. What is the oxidation number of S in the thiosulfate ion $S_2O_3^{2-}$?

    total oxidation number for the ion = -2

    3 O gives oxidation total $3 \times (-2)$ = -6

    oxidation number total for 2 S + (-6) for oxygen = -2

    oxidation number for 2 S = +4

    S has oxidation number +2

4. What is the oxidation number of P in $Ca_3(PO_4)_2$?

    3 Ca with 8 O gives a total $3 \times (+2) + 8 \times (-2)$ = -10

    2 P must have a total oxidation value + 10

    P has an oxidation number +5

PROBLEMS

(ANSWERS ON PAGE 154)

1. State the oxidation numbers of the elements in each formula
(a) Cl_2 (b) H_2 (c) O_3 (d) Cl^- (e) Na^+ (f) P_4 (g) S (h) Mg

2. Calculate the oxidation number of (a) S in BaS (b) C in CO_2
(c) N in HNO_3 (d) P in PO_4^{3-} (e) S in HSO_4^-

III. NAMING THE OXIDIZING AGENT AND THE REDUCING AGENT

In a redox reaction, the oxidizing agent is the substance reduced and the reducing agent is the substance oxidized. For example,

$$2Mg + O_2 \longrightarrow 2 MgO$$

Magnesium as the element uncombined has oxidation number zero.

Similarly oxygen in O_2 has oxidation number zero. In magnesium oxide the Mg has oxidation number +2, and the oxygen -2.

The substance oxidized is Mg (also called the reducing agent) because its oxidation number shows a positive increase from O to +2.

Oxygen of the O_2 is the substance reduced (also called the oxidizing agent) because its oxidation number decreases from O to -2.

The oxidizing agent and the reducing agent are found by calculating the oxidation number for every atom in the reactants and products, and then selecting the atom which increases its oxidation number along with the atom which shows a decrease in oxidation number.

EXAMPLES

1. Name the substance oxidized (reducing agent) and the substance reduced in this reaction:

$$Cu + 4HNO_3 \longrightarrow Cu(NO_3)_2 + 2H_2O + N_2O_4$$

Calculate the oxidation numbers and write them above each atom

$$\overset{0}{Cu} + 4\ \overset{+1}{H}\ \overset{+5}{N}\ \overset{-2}{O_3} \longrightarrow \overset{+2}{Cu}\ (\overset{+5}{N}\ \overset{-2}{O_3})_2 + 2\ \overset{+1}{H_2}\ \overset{-2}{O} + \overset{+4}{N_2}\ \overset{-2}{O_4}$$

Cu is the substance oxidized (the reducing agent) because its oxidation number increases from 0 to +2.

The N of the nitric acid (or the nitric acid) is the substance reduced (oxidizing agent) because its oxidation number decreases from +5 to +4 in forming N_2O_4.

2. Name the oxidizing agent and the reducing agent in this reaction:

$$HI + H_2SO_4 \longrightarrow I_2 + H_2S + H_2O$$

Again, calculate and write in the oxidation numbers.

$$\overset{+1}{H}\ \overset{-1}{I} + \overset{+1}{H_2}\ \overset{+6}{S}\ \overset{-2}{O_4} \longrightarrow \overset{0}{I_2} + \overset{+1}{H_2}\ \overset{-2}{S} + \overset{+1}{H_2}\ \overset{-2}{O}$$

The iodine of the HI increases its oxidation number from -1 to 0 in forming I_2. Therefore the reducing agent or substance oxidized is HI.

The S of the H_2SO_4 is reduced because its oxidation number decreases from +6 to -2 in forming H_2S. Sulfuric acid is the oxidizing agent.

3. Name the substance reduced and the substance oxidized in this reaction:

$$MnO_4^- + H^+ + Cl^- \longrightarrow Mn^{2+} + Cl_2 + H_2O$$

Note that the reaction involves ions and that the equation does not have to be balanced to find the reducing agent and oxidizing agent.

$$\overset{+7}{Mn}\ \overset{-2}{O_4^-} + \overset{+1}{H^+} + \overset{-1}{Cl^-} \longrightarrow \overset{2+}{Mn^{2+}} + \overset{0}{Cl_2} + \overset{+1}{H_2}\ \overset{-2}{O}$$

Mn of the permanganate ion is reduced in going from +7 to +2 of the manganese (II) ion. MnO_4^- is the oxidizing agent. The Cl^- ion is oxidized to Cl_2 and increases its oxidation number.

Note: 1. The equation does not have to be balanced to find the reducing agent and the oxidizing agent.

        2. The reaction is not a reduction-oxidation if there is no change in oxidation number.

        3. The oxidizing agent and reducing agent are always reactants.

IV. BALANCING OF OXIDATION-REDUCTION EQUATIONS

1. Molecular Equations

The general rules for balancing oxidation-reduction equations are as follows:

1. Set down the skeleton equation including all the products of the reaction.

2. Determine the change in valence number of the elements which are being oxidized and reduced.

3. If the number of atoms of the oxidized or reduced element is not equal on both sides of the equation, a preliminary balance will be necessary. Thus if HBr is oxidized to Br_2, it is necessary to have 2 molecules of HBr.

4. Multiply by such numbers so that the number of electrons which is lost by the reducing agent is equal to the number of electrons gained by the oxidizing agent.

5. Balance all salts and acids which form salts.

6. Balance all hydrogens.

7. Check the equation to see if there is an equal number of oxygen atoms on both sides of the equation.

EXAMPLE

1. $\overset{0}{Cu} + \overset{+5}{HNO_3} + H_2SO_4 \longrightarrow \overset{+2}{CuSO_4} + \overset{+2}{NO} + H_2O$

Rules 1 and 2 are illustrated above. Copper increases in valence from O to +2, losing 2 electrons, Copper is oxidized. Nitrogen decreases in valence from +5 to +2, gaining 3 electrons, Nitrogen is reduced. Copper is the reducing agent and nitric acid is the oxidizing agent.

Rule 4 does not apply in this equation since the number of atoms which undergoes oxidation and reduction is the same on both sides of the equation.

Rule 4

$$Cu^° \xrightarrow{-2e} Cu^{+2} \ (-2e) \times 3 = -6e$$
$$N^{+5} \xrightarrow{+3e} N^{+2} \ (+3e) \times 2 = +6e$$

To make the gain and loss of electrons equal, it is necessary to take 3 atoms of copper and 2 atoms of nitrogen. Placing these coefficients into the main equation:

$$3Cu + 2HNO_3 + H_2SO_4 \longrightarrow 3CuSO_4 + 2NO + H_2O$$
(incomplete)

Since 3 atoms of copper are oxidized, 3 molecules of $CuSO_4$ are formed, and since 2 molecules of HNO_3 are reduced, 2 molecules of NO are formed.

Rule 5.   The salts and acids which form salts are now balanced by inspection. Since 3 molecules of $CuSO_4$ are formed, 3 molecules of H_2SO_4 are necessary.

$$3Cu + 2HNO_3 + 3H_2SO_4 \longrightarrow 3CuSO_4 + 2NO + H_2O$$
(incomplete)

Rule 6.   The hydrogens are now balanced. The $2HNO_3$ and $3H_2SO_4$ yield a total of 8 hydrogen atoms; therefore 4 molecules of H_2O are formed.

$$3Cu + 2HNO_3 + 3H_2SO_4 \longrightarrow 3CuSO_4 + 2NO + 4H_2O$$

Rule 7.   Check the oxygen atoms. The sulfate oxygens need not be considered, since there already is an equal number of sulfates on both sides of the equation. $2HNO_3$ yield 6 oxygen atoms, and 2NO and $4H_2O$ also yield 6 oxygen atoms, and thus the equation is balanced.

EXAMPLE

1. $\overset{0}{Cu} + \overset{+5}{HNO_3} \longrightarrow \overset{+2}{Cu}(\overset{+2}{NO_3})_2 + NO + H_2O$ (incomplete)

Rules 1 and 2 are illustrated above, and rule 3 does not apply in the equation.

Rule 4

$$\overset{0}{Cu} \xrightarrow{-2e} \overset{+2}{Cu}(-2e) \times 3 = -6e$$

$$\overset{+5}{N} \xrightarrow{+3e} \overset{+2}{N}(+3e) \times 2 = +6e$$

To make the gain and loss of electrons equal, it is necessary to take 3 atoms of Cu and 3 molecules of $Cu(NO_3)_2$ and 2 molecules of HNO_3 and NO.

$$3Cu + 2HNO_3 \longrightarrow 3Cu(NO_3)_2 + 2NO + H_2O \text{ (incomplete)}$$

Rule 5. The HNO_3 serves 2 purposes in this equation. As an oxidizing agent, 2 molecules of HNO_3 are necessary to oxidize the Cu. The HNO_3 serves also as an acid, forming 3 molecules of $Cu(NO_3)_2$. For this purpose, 6 molecules of HNO_3 are necessary. The total number of molecules of HNO_3 necessary therefore, is 2 plus 6 or 8 molecules. Placing this in the skeleton equation, we have:

$$3Cu + 8HNO_3 \longrightarrow 3Cu(NO_3)_2 + 2NO + H_2O \text{ (incomplete)}$$

Rule 6. Balancing the hydrogen atoms, we have:

$$3Cu + 8HNO_3 \longrightarrow 3Cu(NO_3)_2 + 2NO + 4H_2O$$

Rule 7. Balancing the oxygen atoms, we find that there are 24 atoms of oxygen on each side, and so the equation is balanced.

EXAMPLE

$$1. \overset{+7}{KMnO_4} + \overset{-1}{HCl} \longrightarrow \overset{+2}{MnCl_2} + \overset{0}{Cl_2} + KCl + H_2O \text{ (incomplete)}$$

Rules 1 and 2 are illustrated above. Chlorine increases in valence number from -1 to 0. Mn decreases in valence number from +7 to +2.

Rule 3. Obviously one molecule of HCl cannot form one molecule of Cl_2. Before it is possible to determine the number of electrons which are transferred, it is necessary to make a preliminary balance between HCl and Cl_2. The skeleton equation now becomes:

$$KMnO_4 + 2HCl \longrightarrow MnCl_2 + Cl_2 + KCl + H_2O$$

Rule 4.

$$2Cl^{-1} \xrightarrow{-2e} Cl_2^{\,0} (-2e) \times 5 = -10e$$

$$\overset{+7}{Mn} \xrightarrow{+5e} \overset{+2}{Mn} (+5e) \times 2 = +10e$$

To make the gain and loss of electrons equal, it is necessary to multiply the molecules of HCl and Cl_2 by 5, and to multiply the molecules of $KMnO_4$ and $MnCl_2$ by 2.

$$2KMnO_4 + 10HCl \longrightarrow 2MnCl_2 + 5Cl_2 + 2KCl + H_2O$$
$$\text{(incomplete)}$$

Rule 5.   The HCl plays 2 roles in this equation. As a reducing agent, 10 molecules of HCl are necessary to reduce the Mn. As an acid, HCl forms 2 molecules of $MnCl_2$ and 2 molecules of KCl, or a total of 6 molecules of HCl for the formation of these salts. The total number of HCl molecules which is necessary is:

10 HCl (for reduction of Mn)
 6 HCl (for $MnCl_2$ and KCl formation)
16 HCl (total)

The equation now becomes:

$$2KMnO_4 + 16HCl \longrightarrow 2MnCl_2 + 5Cl_2 + 2KCl + H_2O$$
$$\text{(incomplete)}$$

Rule 6.   Balancing the hydrogen atoms:

$$2KMnO_4 + 16HCl \longrightarrow 2MnCl_2 + 5Cl_2 + 2KCl + 8H_2O$$

Rule 7.   Balancing the oxygen atoms, we find that there are 8 atoms of oxygen on each side of the equation, and so the equation is balanced.

2. Partial Equations.   The Ion-Electron Method.

The ion-electron method of balancing oxidation-reduction equations is preferred by many chemists because it frequently gives a more accurate description of the actual reaction. This method concerns itself only with those ions which react and ignores those which do not react.

The general rules for balancing oxidation-reduction equations by the ion-electron method are as follows:

1. Set down the partial equation including only the oxidizing and reducing agents and H^+ or OH^- if applicable.

2. Determine the valence number of the elements which are being oxidized and reduced.

3. Preliminary balance if necessary.

4. Make the number of electrons gained by the oxidizing agent equal to the number of electrons lost by the reducing agent.

78

5. Neglecting the H^+ or OH^- ions, determine the algebraic sum of the charges of the ions on each side of the equation. Make the algebraic sum of the charges equal by multiplying the H^+ or OH^- by the proper number.

6. Balance the hydrogens.

7. Check the oxygen atoms.

EXAMPLE

1. $\overset{0}{Cu} + H^+ + \overset{+5}{NO_3^-} \longrightarrow \overset{+2}{Cu^{+2}} + NO + H_2O$ (incomplete)

Rules 1 and 2 are illustrated above. Rule 3 does not apply in this case.

Rule 4.

$$Cu^0 \longrightarrow Cu^{+2} \ (-2e) \times 3 = -6e$$
$$N^{+5} \longrightarrow N^{+2} \ (+3e) \times 2 = +6e$$

Placing these coefficients in the equation:

$$3Cu^0 + H^+ + 2NO_3^- \longrightarrow 3Cu^{+2} + 2NO + H_2O \text{ (incomplete)}$$

Rule 5. Neglecting the H^+, the net charge on the left hand side of the equation is -2 ($2NO_3^-$). The net charge on the right hand side of the equation is +6 ($3Cu^{+2}$). To make the algebraic sum on the left equal to +6, eight H^+ ions are necessary.

$$3Cu^0 + 8H^+ + 2NO_3^- \longrightarrow 3Cu^{+2} + 2NO + H_2O \text{ (incomplete)}$$

Rule 6. Balancing the hydrogens we have:

$$3Cu^0 + 8H^+ + 2NO_3^- \longrightarrow 3Cu^{+2} + 2NO + 4H_2O$$

Rule 7. Checking the oxygen atoms we find there are 6 atoms of oxygen on each side.

EXAMPLE

1. $\overset{+7}{MnO_4^-} + H^+ + Br^- \longrightarrow Mn^{+2} + \overset{0}{Br_2} + H_2O$ (incomplete)

Rules 1 and 2 are illustrated above.

Rule 3. A preliminary balance is necessary between Br^{-1} and Br_2.

$$MnO_4^- + H^+ + 2Br^- \longrightarrow Mn^{+2} + \overset{0}{Br_2} + H_2O \text{ (incomplete)}$$

Rule 4.

$$Mn^{+7} \longrightarrow Mn^{+2} \ (+5e) \ \times \ 2 \ = \ +10e$$

$$2Br^{-1} \longrightarrow \overset{0}{Br_2} \ (-2e) \ \times \ 5 \ = \ -10e$$

$$2MnO_4^- + H^+ + 10Br^- \longrightarrow 2Mn^{+2} + 5Br_2 + H_2O \ (incomplete)$$

Rule 5. Neglecting the H^+, the net charge on the left side is -12 ($2MnO_4^- + 10Br^-$) while the net charge on the right side is +4 ($2Mn^{+2}$). To make the algebraic sum on the left side equal to +4, sixteen H^+ ions are necessary.

$$2MnO_4^- + 16H^+ + 10Br^- \longrightarrow 2Mn^{+2} + 5Br_2 + H_2O \ (incomplete)$$

Rule 6. Balancing the hydrogens we have:

$$2MnO_4^- + 16H^+ + 10Br^- \longrightarrow 2Mn^{+2} + 5Br_2 + 8H_2O$$

Rule 7. Checking the oxygen atoms we find there are 8 atoms of oxygen on each side.

EXAMPLE

1. $Cr^{+3} + \overset{0}{Cl_2} + OH^- \longrightarrow \overset{+6}{CrO_4^{-2}} + Cl^- + H_2O$ (incomplete)

Rules 1 and 2 are illustrated above.

Rule 3. A preliminary balance is necessary between Cl_2 and Cl^-

$$Cr^{+3} + Cl_2 + OH^- \longrightarrow CrO_4^{-2} + 2Cl^- + H_2O \ (incomplete)$$

Rule 4.

$$Cr^{+3} \longrightarrow Cr^{+6} \ (-3e) \ \times \ 2 \ = \ -6e$$

$$Cl_2^0 \longrightarrow 2Cl^- \ (+2e) \ \times \ 3 \ = \ +6e$$

$$2Cr^{+3} + 3Cl_2 + OH^- \longrightarrow 2CrO_4^{-2} + 6Cl^- + H_2O \ (incomplete)$$

Rule 5. Neglecting the OH^-, the net charge on the left side is +6 ($2Cr^{+3}$) while the net charge on the right side is -10 ($2CrO_4^{-2} + 6Cl^-$). To make the algebraic sum on the left side equal to -10, sixteen OH^- ions are necessary.

$$2Cr^{+3} + 3Cl_2 + 16OH^- \longrightarrow 2CrO_4^{-2} + 6Cl^- + H_2O \ (incomplete)$$

Rule 6. Balancing the hydrogens we have:

$$2Cr^{+3} + 3Cl_2 + 16OH^- \longrightarrow 2CrO_4^{-2} + 6Cl^- + 8H_2O$$

Rule 7. Checking the oxygen atoms we find there are 16 atoms of oxygen on each side.

PROBLEMS

(ANSWERS ON PAGE 155)

1. $H_2S + HNO_3 \longrightarrow S + NO + H_2O$

2. $H_2S + HNO_3 \longrightarrow H_2SO_4 + NO_2 + H_2O$

3. $HI + H_2SO_4 \longrightarrow I_2 + H_2S + H_2O$

4. $HBr + H_2SO_4 \longrightarrow Br_2 + SO_2 + H_2O$

5. $KMnO_4 + HBr \longrightarrow Br_2 + MnBr_2 + KBr + H_2O$

6. $KMnO_4 + H_2S + H_2SO_4 \longrightarrow S + MnSO_4 + K_2SO_4 + H_2O$

7. $K_2Cr_2O_7 + H_2S + H_2SO_4 \longrightarrow S + Cr_2(SO_4)_3 + K_2SO_4 + H_2O$

8. $S + H_2SO_4 \longrightarrow SO_2 + H_2O$

9. $NaOH + Br_2 \longrightarrow NaBrO_3 + NaBr + H_2O$

10. $S + HNO_3 \longrightarrow H_2SO_4 + NO_2 + H_2O$

Balance each of the following equations by the ion-electron method.

1. $S^{-2} + H^+ + NO_3^- \longrightarrow S + NO + H_2O$

2. $Pb^0 + H^+ + NO_3^- \longrightarrow Pb^{+2} + NO_2 + H_2O$

3. $Cd^0 + H^+ + NO_3^- \longrightarrow Cd^{+2} + NO + H_2O$

4. $MnO_4^- + H^+ + Cl^- \longrightarrow Mn^{+2} + Cl_2 + H_2O$

5. $MnO_4^- + H^+ + S^{-2} \longrightarrow Mn^{+2} + S + H_2O$

6. $Cr_2O_7^{-2} + H^+ + S^{-2} \longrightarrow S + Cr^{+3} + H_2O$

PREDICTING PRODUCTS OF OXIDATION-REDUCTION REACTIONS

I. COMMON REDUCING AGENTS

Reducing Agent	Product Oxidized To:
1. Alkali metals (Li, Na, K, etc.)	Li^+, Na^+, K^+, etc.

$$4Li + O_2 \longrightarrow 2Li_2O$$
$$2K + Cl_2 \longrightarrow 2KCl$$

2. Most metals or   ————————→ Highest valence state
   metal ions   of metal

$$Cu + Cl_2 \longrightarrow CuCl_2$$
$$2FeCl_2 + Cl_2 \longrightarrow 2FeCl_3$$

3. Hydrogen ————————————→ H^+ or H_2O

$$H_2 + Cl_2 \longrightarrow 2HCl$$
$$H_2 + CuO \longrightarrow Cu + H_2O$$

4. Carbon monoxide ——————————→ CO_2

$$2CO + O_2 \longrightarrow 2CO_2$$
$$3CO + Fe_2O_3 \longrightarrow 2Fe + 3CO_2$$

5. H_2S and $S^=$ $\xrightarrow{\text{all oxidizing agents} \atop \text{except conc. } HNO_3}$ S

$$3CuS + 8HNO_3 \text{ (dil)} \longrightarrow 3S + 3Cu(NO_3)_2 + 2NO + 4H_2O$$
$$3H_2S + K_2Cr_2O_7 + 4H_2SO_4 \longrightarrow 3S + Cr_2(SO_4)_3 + K_2SO_4 + 7H_2O$$

6. H_2S and $S^=$ $\xrightarrow{\text{Conc. } HNO_3}$ $SO_4^=$

$$H_2S + 8HNO_3 \text{ (conc)} \longrightarrow H_2SO_4 + 8NO_2 + 4H_2O$$

7. So_2 or $SO_3^=$ ——————————→ $SO_4^=$

$$H_2SO_3 + 2HNO_3 \text{ (conc)} \longrightarrow H_2SO_4 + 2NO_2 + H_2O$$
$$2KMnO_4 + 5SO_2 + 2H_2O \longrightarrow K_2SO_4 + 2MnSO_4 + 2H_2SO_4$$

8. Halides (Cl^-, Br^-, I^-) ——————→ Free Halogen (Cl_2, Br_2, I_2)

$$MnO_2 + 4HCl \longrightarrow Cl_2 + MnCl_2 + 2H_2O$$

9. HNO_2 ———————————————→ HNO_3

$$5HNO_2 + 2KMnO_4 + 3H_2SO_4 \longrightarrow 5HNO_3 + 2MnSO_4 + K_2SO_4 + 3H_2O$$

10. H_2O_2 ———————————————→ O_2

$$5H_2O_2 + 2KMnO_4 + 3H_2SO_4 \longrightarrow K_2SO_4 + 2MnSO_4 + 5O_2 + 8H_2O$$

II. COMMON OXIDIZING AGENTS

Oxidizing Agent   **Product Reduced To:**

1. O_2 ————————————————→ $O^=$ or H_2O

$$2Ca + O_2 \longrightarrow 2CaO$$
$$2H_2 + O_2 \longrightarrow 2H_2O$$

2. Halogens (Cl_2, Br_2, I_2) ──────────→ Halides $(Cl^-, Br^-, I^-,)$

$Zn + Br_2$ ──────→ $ZnBr_2$

3. Dilute HNO_3 ──────────────→ NO

$3Cu + 8HNO_3(dil)$ ──────→ $3Cu(NO_3)_2 + 2NO + 4H_2O$

4. Concentrated HNO_3 ──────────→ NO_2

$Cu + 4HNO_3 (Conc)$ ──────→ $Cu(NO_3)_2 + 2NO_2 + 2H_2O$

5. H_2SO_4 (Hot & Conc) ──────────→ SO_2

$Cu + 2H_2SO_4$ (hot & conc) ──────→ $CuSO_4 + SO_2 + 2H_2O$

6. MnO_4^- or MnO_2 (acid solution) ──────→ Mn^{++}

$2KMnO_4 + 5H_2S + 3H_2SO_4$ ──────→ $5S + 2MnSO_4 + K_2SO_4 + 8H_2O$

7. MnO_4^- (neutral or basic solution) ──────→ MnO_2

$KMnO_4 + 3NO_2 + 2KOH$ ──────→ $3KNO_3 + MnO_2 + H_2O$

8. $Cr_2O_7^=$ or $CrO_4^=$ ──────────────→ Cr^{+++}

$K_2Cr_2O_7 + 14HCl$ ──────→ $2CrCl_3 + 2KCl + 3Cl_2 + 7H_2O$

9. HNO_2 ──────────────────→ NO

$2HNO_2 + 2HI$ ──────→ $I_2 + 2NO + 2H_2O$

10. H_2O_2 ──────────────────────→ H_2O

$2HI + H_2O_2$ ──────────→ $2H_2O + I_2$

EXAMPLES

1. Predict the products of the following reaction.

$$KMnO_4 + H_2S + H_2SO_4 \longrightarrow$$

The oxidizing agent here is $KMnO_4$; the reducing agent is H_2S.

The H_2SO_4 is present to make the solution acidic, since only hot and concentrated H_2SO_4 acts as an oxidizing agent. The $KMnO_4$ will be reduced, and the H_2S will be oxidized. In an acid medium, $KMnO_4$ will be reduced to Mn^{++} and the H_2S will be oxidized to S^0, since only concentrated HNO_3 will oxidize $S^=$ to $SO_4^=$. In the presence of H_2SO_4, K^+ and Mn^{++} form sulfates. The hydrogen from the H_2SO_4 and H_2S, and the oxygen from $KMnO_4$ will form water. The complete equation is:

$$2KMnO_4 + 5H_2S + 3H_2SO_4 \longrightarrow 2MnSO_4 + 5S + K_2SO_4 + 8H_2O$$

2. Predict the products of the following reaction.

$$H_2S + HNO_3 \text{ (conc)} \longrightarrow$$

The oxidizing agent is concentrated HNO_3, and the reducing agent is H_2S. The $S^=$ will be oxidized to $SO_4^=$ by the concentrated HNO_3, and the concentrated HNO_3 is reduced to NO_2. The complete equation is:

$$H_2S + 8HNO_3 \text{ (conc)} \longrightarrow H_2SO_4 + 8NO_2 + 4H_2O$$

PROBLEMS

(ANSWERS ON PAGE 155)

Complete and balance the following equations:

1. $CO + O_2$
2. $Cu + HNO_3$ (conc)
3. $Fe + HNO_3$ (dil)
4. $FeSO_4 + HNO_3$ (dil) $+ H_2SO_4$
5. $H_2SO_3 + HNO_3$ (conc)
6. $HBr + KMnO_4$
7. $HBr + K_2Cr_2O_7$
8. $NaCl + MnO_2 + H_2SO_4$
9. $H_2S + KMnO_4 + H_2SO_4$
10. $H_2S + K_2Cr_2O_7 + H_2SO_4$

ATOMIC WEIGHTS

I. LAW OF DULONG AND PETIT

DuLong and Petit discovered that the product of the atomic weight and the specific heat of most solid elements is approximately 6.4. This value is the number of calories required to raise the temperature of one gram atom of most solid elements one degree centigrade. Thus:

$$\text{Specific heat} \times \text{atomic weight} = 6.4 \text{ (approx.)}$$

If the specific heat of a solid element is known, the approximate atomic weight of the element may be calculated.

$$\frac{6.4}{\text{Specific heat}} = \text{approximate atomic weight}$$

EXAMPLE

1. Lead has a specific heat of 0.0305 cal per gram. What is the approximate atomic weight of lead?

$$\text{approx. at. wt.} = \frac{6.4}{\text{sp. ht.}}$$

$$= \frac{6.4}{0.0305}$$

$$= 209.6$$

II. VALENCE, EQUIVALENT WEIGHT AND ATOMIC WEIGHT

The valence of an element may be defined as the number of atoms of hydrogen which one atom of the element combines with or displaces. Thus, since one atom of chlorine combines with one atom of hydrogen, the valence of chlorine is 1. One atom of oxygen combines with 2 atoms of hydrogen; therefore the valence of oxygen is 2.

The equivalent weight of an element has been defined as the number of grams of the element which will combine with or displace 1 gram atomic weight of hydrogen. Since 8 grams of oxygen combine with 1 gram of hydrogen, the equivalent weight of oxygen is 8 g (1/2 atomic weight); and since 1 gram-atom (16 g) of oxygen combines with 2 gram-atoms of hydrogen, it follows that:

$$\text{equivalent weight} = \frac{\text{atomic weight}}{\text{valence}}$$

or

$$\text{valence} = \frac{\text{atomic weight}}{\text{equivalent weight}}$$

EXAMPLE

1. The atomic weight of an element is 27 and the equivalent weight is 9 g. Calculate the valence of the element.

$$\text{Valence} = \frac{\text{atomic weight}}{\text{equivalent weight}}$$

$$= \frac{27}{9}$$

$$= 3$$

Since atoms are not divisible, valence must be a whole number.

III. EXACT ATOMIC WEIGHTS

If the approximate atomic weight and the equivalent weight of an element are known, the valence and the exact atomic weight may then be calculated.

EXAMPLE

1. The specific heat of an element is 0.113 cal per gram, and 10.47 g of this element combine with 3 g of oxygen. Calculate the exact atomic weight.

The approximate atomic weight may be calculated from the law of DuLong and Petit.

$$\text{approx. atomic weight} = \frac{6.4}{0.113}$$

$$= 56.6$$

Since 10.47 g of the element combine with 3 g of oxygen, the equivalent weight of the element may be calculated:

3 g of O_2 combine with 10.47 g of the element

then, 1 g of O_2 combines with $\frac{10.47}{3}$ g of the element.

and 8 g of O_2 combine with $8 \times \frac{10.47}{3} = 27.92$ g (equivalent weight of the element)

Then

$$\text{valence} = \frac{\text{atomic weight}}{\text{equivalent weight}}$$

$$= \frac{56.6}{27.92} \text{ (approx. at. wt.)}$$

$$= 2.03$$

Since valence must be a whole number, the valence must be 2. The exact atomic weight is

$$\text{atomic weight} = \text{equivalent weight} \times \text{valence}$$

$$= 27.92 \times 2$$

$$= 55.84$$

IV. ATOMIC NUMBER AND MASS NUMBER

Atomic Number.   This is the positive charge of the nucleus of an atom, and therefore the number of protons in the nucleus. It is written as a subscript to the symbol of the element, as in $_{17}Cl$ and $_{92}U$.

Cl atoms have 17 protons in each nucleus, all uranium atoms have 92 protons in the nucleus.

Atoms are electrically neutral. Therefore the number of electrons in energy shells outside the nucleus equals the number of protons in the nucleus, as in $_{11}Na$, sodium atoms have 11 protons and 11 electrons.

Mass Number.   This is the sum of the protons and neutrons in the nucleus of an atom. It is written as a superscript, Cl^{35}, U^{238} etc.

Mass number also give the mass of an atom in amu, because neutrons and protons are approximately 1 amu each in mass, and electrons have relatively very little mass.

Isotopes.   Atoms of the same element differing in mass only, because of a different number of neutrons in the nucleus. U-235 and U-238 are uranium isotopes, Cl^{35} and Cl^{37} are chlorine isotopes.

It follows that

number of neutrons in the nucleus

= Mass Number (sum of protons and neutrons)

- Atomic Number (number of protons)

EXAMPLES

1. The $_{17}Cl^{35}$ isotope has   35 protons + neutrons

$\underline{- 17}$ protons

= 18 neutrons

The $_{17}Cl^{37}$ isotope has   37 protons + neutrons

$\underline{- 17}$ protons

= 20 neutrons

2. What is the composition of the isotopes $_{92}U^{235}$ and $_{92}U^{238}$?

Atomic number = 92   each atom has 92 protons, therefore 92 electrons

U-235 has 235 - 92 = 143 neutrons

U-238 has 238 - 92 = 145 neutrons

With few exceptions the isotopes of an element are chemically identical because they have the same number of electrons. It is the electron structure which determines chemical properties.

Atomic Weight and Isotope Weights.

Most of the known elements occur in nature as mixtures of their isotopes. The atomic weight of an element is the average of the weights of the isotopes taking account of their relative abundance.

EXAMPLES

1. Chlorine occurs in nature as the isotopes Cl^{35} and Cl^{37}.

   There are approximately 3 Cl^{35} atoms for every 1 Cl^{37} atom in any natural sample of chlorine or its compounds.

   $$\text{Atomic Weight} = \frac{\text{total weight of sample}}{\text{number of atoms in sample}}$$

   $$= \frac{(3 \times 35) + (1 \times 37)}{4} = \frac{105 + 37}{4} = 35.5$$

2. Calculate the relative abundance of the B^{10} and B^{11} isotopes if the atomic weight of boron is 10.8.

   Let there be 1 B^{10} atom for every m B^{11} atoms.

   Number of atoms in the sample = 1 + m

   $$\text{Atomic Weight, } 10.8 = \frac{(1 \times 10) + (m \times 11)}{m + 1}$$

   $$10.8 = \frac{10 + 11m}{m + 1}$$

   $$10.8 (m + 1) = 10 + 11m$$

   $$10.8 m + 10.8 = 10 + 11m$$

   $$0.8 = 0.2m$$

   $$m = 4$$

There are 4 B^{11} atoms for every 1 B^{10} atom.

88

PROBLEMS

(ANSWERS ON PAGE 155)

1. Calculate the approximate atomic weights of elements which have the following specific heats. (a) 0.23 calories, (b) 0.14 calories, (c) 0.082 calories, (d) 0.063 calories.

2. The equivalent weight of a metal is 68.9 g and its specific heat is 0.0305 calories. Determine (a) the valence and (b) the exact atomic weight of the metal.

3. The equivalent weight of magnesium is 12.16 and its specific heat is 0.247 calories. Calculate (a) the valence and (b) the exact atomic weight of magnesium.

4. When 4.5 g of Al were dissolved in excess acid, 5.6 liters of H_2 at STP were evolved. Calculate (a) the equivalent weight and (b) the valence of aluminum.

5. Analysis shows that 8.1 g of an oxide contain 5.66 g of a metal. The specific heat of the metal is 0.113 calories. Calculate the exact atomic weight of the metal.

6. Analysis shows that 0.26 g of an element combines with 0.12 g of oxygen. The specific heat of the element is 0.128 calories. Calculate the exact atomic weight of the element.

7. Analysis of a chloride of an element shows that the chloride contains 25.46% of the element. The specific heat of the element is 0.262 calories. Calculate the exact atomic weight of the element.

8. It was found that 16 parts by weight of oxygen combine with 37.23 parts by weight of a metal. The specific heat of this metal is 0.106 calories. Calculate the exact atomic weight of the metal.

9. The specific heat of an element is 0.066 calories. It was found that 4.570 g of the element form 10.00 g of the fluoride. If the equivalent weight of fluorine is 19.00 g, calculate the exact atomic weight of the element.

10. State the number of protons, electrons, and neutrons in each of the following atoms:

   (a) $_1H^2$ (b) $_8O^{16}$ (c) $_{13}Al^{27}$ (d) $_{93}Np^{238}$

11. Copper occurs naturally as the isotopes Cu-63 (approximately 70%) and Cu-65 (approximately 30%). Calculate the atomic weight.

EXPRESSING CONCENTRATION OF SOLUTIONS

I. INTRODUCTION

A solution has been defined as a homogeneous mixture of two or more substances, the composition of which may be varied. The dissolved substance is usually called the solute, and the medium in which it is dissolved is called the solvent. The solvent is generally the component which is present in the larger quantity.

A standard solution is one whose concentration is known. This section will deal with standard solutions, both dilute and concentrated.

II. METHODS OF EXPRESSING CONCENTRATION OF SOLUTIONS

A. WEIGHT OF SOLUTE PER 100 GRAMS OF SOLVENT

If a solution contains 4.6 g of solute material in 24.8 g of the solvent, the concentration of the solution is known from this statement as it stands. Comparison of the concentrations of different solutions is easier if the number of grams of solute per 100 grams of solvent is used.

EXAMPLES

1. A solution contains 11.3 g of solute in 56.4 g of water. Express the concentration in grams of solute per 100 grams of water.

$$56.4 \text{ g water contain } 11.3 \text{ g solute}$$

$$1 \text{ g of water contains } \frac{11.3}{56.4} \text{ g solute}$$

$$100 \text{ g water contains } 100 \times \frac{11.3}{56.4} \text{ g solute}$$

$$= 20.0 \text{ g solute}$$

The concentration is 20.0 g solute per 100 g water.

2. A solution of a salt in water weighs 1260 g and contains 147 g of the salt. Express the concentration of the salt in grams per 100 g of water.

$$1260 \text{ g solution} - 147 \text{ g salt} = 1113 \text{ g water}$$

$$1113 \text{ g water contain } 147 \text{ g salt}$$

90

$$1 \text{ g water contains } \frac{147}{1113} \text{ g salt}$$

$$100 \text{ g water contain } 100 \times \frac{147}{1113} = 13.2 \text{ g salt}$$

B. PERCENTAGE SOLUTE IN THE SOLUTION

This method of stating concentration differs from the preceding examples. Express the concentration in grams of solute per 100 grams of solution. For example, a 4% solution of common salt in water contains 4 g of salt in 96 g of water. The weight of the solution is taken as the 100%.

EXAMPLES

1. A solution contains 15 g of solute in 60 g of water. State the concentration in g solute per 100 g of solution.

$$15 \text{ g solute} + 60 \text{ g water} = 75 \text{ g solution}$$

$$75 \text{ g solution contains } 15 \text{ g solute}$$

$$1 \text{ g solution contains } \frac{15}{75} \text{ g solute}$$

$$100 \text{ g solution contains } 100 \times \frac{15}{75} = 20 \text{ g solute}$$

It is a 20% solution of the solute.

2. What weight of sodium hydroxide is in 1600 g of a 12% solution?

$$100 \text{ g solution contains } 12 \text{ g sodium hydroxide}$$

$$1 \text{ g solution contains } \frac{12}{100} \text{ g sodium hydroxide}$$

$$1600 \text{ g solution contains } 1600 \times \frac{12}{100} = 192 \text{ g sodium hydroxide}$$

C. MOLARITY

Molarity is defined as the number of moles of solute per liter of solution. A 1 molar (1 M) solution contains 1 mole of the solute in 1 liter of total solution. An 18 molar solution of hydrogen sulfate (H_2SO_4) contains 18 moles of this substance added to sufficient water to make the final volume of the solution 1 liter.

In a 0.4 M solution of sodium hydroxide there is 0.4×40 g of sodium hydroxide dissolved in water to make a solution of volume 1 liter.
1 mole of NaOH is $23 + 16 + 1 = 40$ g.

EXAMPLES

1. What weight of hydrogen sulfate is present in 1 liter of 18 M sulfuric acid?   H = 1, S = 32, O = 16

   H_2SO_4 1 mole = 98 g

   A 1 molar solution of this acid contains 98 g H_2SO_4 in 1 liter of solution.

   An 18 M solution contains 18×98 = 1764 g H_2SO_4 in 1 liter of solution.

2. What weight of sodium hydroxide is in 200 ml of a 0.6 M solution?

   NaOH 1 mole = 23 + 16 + 1 = 40 g

   200 ml = 0.2 liter

   1 liter of 0.6 M solution contains 0.6 moles solute

   0.2 liter contains 0.2×0.6 = 0.12 moles solute

   0.12 moles of NaOH is 0.12×40 = 4.8 g

3. Calculate the molarity of a solution containing 68 g of sodium nitrate in 1 liter of solution.

   $NaNO_3$ 1 mole   23 + 14 + (3 × 16) = 85 g

   85 g $NaNO_3$ in 1 liter of solution is 1 M

   1 g $NaNO_3$ in 1 liter of solution is $\frac{1}{85}$ M

   68 g $NaNO_3$ in 1 liter of solution is $68 \times \frac{1}{85}$ = 0.8 M

4. What is the molarity of a solution of nitric acid if it is 71% pure hydrogen nitrate (HNO_3) and has a specific gravity of 1.43?

   HNO_3 1 mole = 1 + 14 + (3 × 16) = 63 g

   1 ml of nitric acid solution weighs 1.43 g

   1 liter of the acid weighs 1000×1.43 = 1430 g

   and is $\frac{71}{100}$ by weight hydrogen nitrate.

   Therefore 1 liter of acid solution contains 0.71×1430 g HNO_3

   $$= 1015 \text{ g}$$

   1 liter of acid containing 63 g HNO_3 is 1 M

   1 liter of acid containing 1015 g is $\frac{1015}{63}$ = 16 M

D. NORMALITY

A normal solution contains one gram equivalent weight of solute in 1 liter of solution. Therefore a 4.5 normal (4.5 N) solution has 4.5 gram equivalents of the solute in 1 liter of solution and a 0.02 N solution has 0.02 gram equivalents of solute in 1 liter of solution.

Elements and compounds react in the proportion of their equivalents. The equivalent weight of an element is found using the relationship

ATOMIC WEIGHT = EQUIVALENT WEIGHT × VALENCE

EXAMPLES: oxygen, atomic weight 16 and valence 2, has an equivalent weight of 8. $16 = 8 \times 2$

aluminum, atomic weight 27 and valence 3, has equivalent weight 9. $27 = 9 \times 3$

hydrogen, atomic weight 1 and valence 1, has an equivalent weight of 1. $1 = 1 \times 1$

The equivalent weight of most compounds, especially acids, bases and salts is found by dividing the formula weight by the total valence of the positive radical or ion.

EXAMPLES:

i) Sulfuric acid H_2SO_4 has formula weight 98, and two H atoms each with a valence +1. The total positive valence is +2, and the equivalent weight is $\frac{98}{2} = 49$.

ii) Calcium hydroxide $Ca(OH)_2$ has formula weight 74, and a total positive valence of +2 because of the one Ca ion. Thus the equivalent of this compound is $\frac{74}{2} = 37$.

iii) Aluminum sulfate $Al_2(SO_4)_3$ formula weight = 342 total positive valence +6 because there are two Al ions each with a valence of +3.

The equivalent weight of the salt is $\frac{342}{6} = 57$.

Normality Calculations

1. What is the normality of a solution containing 60 g of sodium hydroxide in 1 liter of solution?

NaOH formula weight (1 mole) 23 + 16 + 1 = 40 g

total positive valence (Na) +1

equivalent weight $\frac{40}{1}$ = 40

40 g NaOH in 1 liter of solution is 1 N

60 g NaOH in 1 liter of solution is $\frac{60}{40}$ = 1.5 N

2. Calculate the number of grams of solute in 200 ml of 2.5 N H_2SO_4 solution.

H_2SO_4 equivalent weight = $\frac{\text{formula weight}}{2}$ = $\frac{98}{2}$ = 49

200 ml = 0.2 liter

1 liter of 1 N H_2SO_4 solution contains 49 g H_2SO_4

0.2 liter of 2.5 N solution contains 0.2 × 2.5 × 49

= 24.5 g pure H_2SO_4

Calculations with normalities are similar to the molarity problems shown in section C. Use equivalent weights of the compounds in the normality calculations, and the formula weights (weight of 1 mole) in molarity calculations.

E. MOLALITY

The molality of a solution is the number of moles of solute in 1000 g of solvent. For example, a 3 molal solution contains 3 moles of solute in 1000 g of solvent, and a 0.25 molal solution of sulfuric acid contains 0.25 moles of hydrogen sulfate in 1000 g of water.

1. Calculate the molality of a solution which contains 10 g of NaOH dissolved in 250 g of water.

NaOH 1 mole = 40 g Therefore 10 g = $\frac{10}{40}$ = 0.25 mole

If 250 g of water contain 0.25 mole of NaOH

1000 g of water contain $\frac{100 \times 0.25}{250}$ = 1 mole

the solution is 1 molal

III. DILUTION PROBLEMS

When a solution is diluted more solvent is added but the quantity of solute is unchanged. The concentration of the solution decreases and its volume increases.

Example.   1 liter of a 1.5 M solution of HCl contains 1.5 moles of hydrogen chloride in 1 liter of solution. If water is added to make the volume of the solution 3 liters, there is a concentration of 1.5 moles in 3 liters which works out to be 0.5 moles in each liter. The diluted solution still contains 1.5 moles of HCl but has a molarity of 0.5

In problems on dilution, the following relationship applies:

volume of concentrated solution × molarity of concentrated solution

   = volume of diluted solution × molarity of diluted solution

   or $V_1 \times M_1 = V_2 \times M_2$

The volumes should be stated in the same units.

        The relationship applies because

number of moles in a solution = volume (in liters) × molarity

3 liters of a 6 molar solution contains 3 × 6 = 18 moles of solute

2 liters of a 9 molar solution contains 2 × 9 = 18 moles of solute

        3 liters × 6 moles = 2 liters × 9 moles

1. 3.5 liters of a 4 molar solution of H_2SO_4 is diluted to a volume of 28 liters. What is the molarity of the dilute solution?

$$V_1 \times M_1 = V_2 \times M_2$$
$$3.5 \times 4 = 28 \times M_2$$
$$M_2 = 0.5$$

The dilute solution is 0.5 molar.

What volume of a 12 M HCl solution is required to make 600 ml of a 0.25 M solution of hydrochloric acid?

   600 ml = 0.6 liter

$$V_1 \times M_1 = V_2 \times M_2$$
$$V_1 \times 12 = 0.6 \times 0.25$$
$$V_1 = 0.0125 \text{ liter (12.5 ml)}$$

A similar formula applies in dilution problems when the concentration is stated in normality

$$V_1 \times N_1 = V_2 \times N_2$$

Again the volume units should be the same.

number of gram equivalent in a solution = volume (in liters)

$\times$ normality

200 ml of a 4 N solution contains $0.2 \times 4 = 0.8$ gram equivalents of the solute

1.6 liters of a 0.5 N solution contains $1.6 \times 0.5 = 0.8$ gram equivalents of the solute, and

$$0.2 \times 4 = 1.6 \times 0.5$$
$$V_1 \times N_1 = V_2 \times N_2$$

The dilution relationship applies not only for molarity and normality and may be stated in the general form:

volume of solution$_1$ $\times$ concentration of solution$_1$

= volume of solution$_2$ $\times$ concentration of solution$_2$

if the volume units are the same and the concentration units are also the same.

EXAMPLE

How many ml of concentrated sulfuric acid, specific gravity 1.86 containing 95% H_2SO_4 by weight must be used to prepare 100 ml of 1 N solution?

1 ml of the concentrated acid solution weighs 1.86 g and contains $0.95 \times 1.86 = 1.757$ g H_2SO_4

The concentration is 1.757 g per ml

A 1 N H_2SO_4 solution contains 49 g per liter or 0.49 g per ml

volume$_1$ $\times$ concentration$_1$ = volume$_2$ $\times$ concentration$_2$

volume$_1$ $\times$ 1.757 = 100 ml $\times$ 0.049

$$\text{volume}_1 = \frac{100 \times 0.049}{1.757} = 2.8 \text{ ml}$$

PROBLEMS

(ANSWERS ON PAGE 156)

1. Calculate the equivalent weights of each of the following compounds. (a) Na_2CO_3, (b) $Na_2CO_3 . 10H_2O$, (c) Na_2SO_4, (d) H_3PO_4, (e) $Ca(OH)_2$, (f) HBr, (g) $AlCl_3$.

2. Calculate the percentage of the following solutions (a) 10 g of NaOH + 40 g H_2O, (b) 2 g of Na_2SO_4 + 18 g of H_2O, (c) 30 g H_2SO_4 + 170 g H_2O, (d) 50 g NaCl + 450 g H_2O.

3. Calculate the number of g in 200 g of (a) 20% KOH, (b) 5% KCl, (c) 40% Na_2SO_4, (d) 15% LiCl, (e) 25% NaOH.

4. Calculate the molarity of each of the following solutions: (a) 50 g NaOH in 400 ml of solution, (b) 20 g $CuSO_4 . 5H_2O$ in 250 ml of solution, (c) 100 g $Na_2CO_3 : 10H_2O$ in 500 ml of solution, (d) 5 g $Al_2 (SO_4)_3$ in 50 ml of solution, (e) 20 g H_2SO_4 in 200 ml of solution.

5. Calculate the number of grams of solute in each of the following solutions: (a) 50 ml of 0.2 M NaOH, (b) 50 ml of 0.02 M $Na_2CO_3 . 10H_2O$, (c) 4 liters of 4 M HCl, (d) 20 liters of 2 M $CuSO_4 . 5H_2O$, (e) 200 ml of 0.3 M H_3PO_4.

6. Calculate the nomality of each of the following solutions: (a) 50 g NaOH in 400 ml of solution, (b) 20 g $CuSO_4 . 5H_2O$ in 250 ml of solution, (c) 100 g $Na_2CO_3 . 10H_2O$ in 500 ml of solution, (d) 5 g $Al_2(SO_4)_3$ in 50 ml of solution, (e) 20 g H_2SO_4 in 200 ml of solution.

7. Calculate the number of grams of solute in each of the following solutions: (a) 200 ml of 2 N H_2SO_4, (b) 150 ml of 0.04 N $Na_2CO_3 . 10H_2O$, (c) 250 ml of 5 N $Al_2(SO_4)_3$, (d) 3 liters of 0.04 N H_3PO_4, (e) 300 ml of 4 N Na_3PO_4.

8. Calculate the molality of each of the following solutions: (a) 40 g of Na_2SO_4 in 400 g of water, (b) 100 g of $Na_2CO_3 . 10H_2O$ in 250 g of water, (c) 20 g of NaOH in 200 g of water, (d) 90 g of $C_6H_{12}O_6$ in 500 g of water, (e) 5 g of KOH in 400 g of water.

9. To what extent must 500 ml of a 5 N solution of H_2SO_4 be diluted to form (a) 2 N solution, (b) 2 M solution?

10. Concentrated H_2SO_4 solution has a sp.gr. of 1.86 and contains 95% of H_2SO_4 by weight. Calculate the number of ml of concentrated acid solution which must be used to form (a) 50 ml of 2 N

solution, (b) 200 ml of 4 N solution, (c) 400 ml of 3 M solution,
(d) 250 ml of 1.5 M solution.

11. Concentrated nitric acid solution has a specific gravity of 1.42
    and contains 70% HNO_3 by weight. Calculate the number of ml
    of 4 N HNO_3 that can be prepared from 50 ml of the concentrated
    HNO_3 solution.

12. Calculate the number of ml of concentrated HCl (sp.gr. 1.19,
    containing 38% HCl by weight) required to prepare 18 liters of
    0.02 N acid solution.

PROPERTIES OF IDEAL SOLUTIONS
I. MOLE FRACTIONS

The mole fraction of solute may be defined as the number of moles of
solute divided by the total number of moles present.

$$\text{Mole fraction of solute} = \frac{\text{moles of solute}}{\text{moles of solute + moles of solvent}}$$

The mole fraction of solvent will then be the number of moles of
solvent divided by the total number of moles present.

$$\text{Mole fraction of solvent} = \frac{\text{moles of solvent}}{\text{moles of solute + moles of solvent}}$$

EXAMPLE

1. Calculate the mole fraction of CH_3OH in a solution which contains
   64 g of CH_3OH in 144 g of water.

$$\text{Moles } CH_3OH = \frac{64 \text{ g}}{32 \text{ g/mole}} = 2 \text{ moles}$$

$$\text{Moles } H_2O = \frac{144 \text{ g}}{18 \text{ g/mole}} = 8 \text{ moles}$$

$$\text{Mole fraction } CH_3OH = \frac{\text{moles } CH_3OH}{\text{moles } CH_3OH + \text{moles } H_2O} = \frac{2}{2 + 8} = 0.2$$

The sum of the mole fractions in a solution must be 1. Mole fraction
may be converted to mole percent by multiplying by 100.

II. VAPOR PRESSURE OF IDEAL SOLUTIONS

Raoult's Law states that in dilute solutions of non-volatile, non-
electrolytes the vapor pressure lowering is proportional to the mole

fraction of the solute molecules, or the vapor pressure of a solution is proportional to the mole fraction of the solvent molecules.

Vapor pressure lowering = vapor pressure of solvent × mole fraction of solute

and

Vapor pressure of solution = vapor pressure of solvent × mole fraction of solvent

EXAMPLE

1. Calculate the vapor pressure of a solution that contains 184 g of glycerol $C_3H_8O_3$, in 144 g of water at $20°C$. The vapor pressure of H_2O at $20°C$ is 17.37 mm.

V.P. sol'n = V.P. solvent × mole fraction of solvent.

The mole fraction of H_2O (solvent) = $\dfrac{\text{moles solvent}}{\text{moles solute + moles solvent}}$

$$= \dfrac{\dfrac{144 \text{ g}}{18 \text{ g/mole}}}{\dfrac{184 \text{ g}}{92 \text{ g/mole}} + \dfrac{144 \text{ g}}{18 \text{ g/mole}}}$$

V.P. sol'n = 17.37 × 0.8 $= \dfrac{8}{2 + 8} = 0.8$

= 13.896 mm.

III. MOLECULAR WEIGHT DETERMINATIONS

Molecular weights of substances that are not volatile may be calculated from freezing point depressions and boiling point elevations. The depression of the freezing point of a solvent which is caused by 1 mole of a non-electrolyte dissolved in 1000 g of solvent (1 molal solution) is known as the molal freezing point constant. The molal freezing point constants are different for each solvent. For aqueous solutions, the molal freezing point constants are different for each solute.   For aqueous solutions, the molal freezing point constant is 1.86°C. Thus, it is possible to state the following expression:

Depression of the freezing point = Molality × (1.86°C)
or since molality is the number of moles per 1000 g of solvent,

Depression of freezing point = $\dfrac{\text{g of solute per 1000 g solvent}}{\text{molecular weight of solute}} \times (1.86°C)$

EXAMPLES

1. The molecular weight of a non-electrolyte is 46. Calculate the freezing point of a solution that contains 30 g of this solute in 500 g of water.

> In 1000 g of water there will be
>
> $$30 \text{ g} \times \frac{1000}{500} = 60 \text{ g of solute}$$
>
> Depression of freezing point, $\Delta t_f = \frac{60}{46} \times (1.86°C)$
>
> $$= 2.425°C$$

Since the freezing point of water is 0°C, the freezing point of the solution will be

$$0° - 2.425° = -2.425°C$$

2. A solution of a non-electrolyte containing 25 g of solute in 200 g of water has a freezing point of -0.93°C. Calculate the molecular weight of the solute.

In 1000 g of water there will be:

$$25 \text{ g} \times \frac{1000}{200} = 125 \text{ g solute}$$

$$\Delta t_f = \frac{\text{g solute per 1000 g of solvent}}{\text{molecular weight of solute}} = (1.86°C)$$

$$0.93 = \frac{125}{\text{Molecular weight}} \times (1.86°C)$$

Molecular weight $= \frac{125}{0.93°C} \times (1.86°C) = 250$

Molecular weights may also be determined by means of the elevation of the boiling point. The molal boiling point elevation constant for aqueous solution is 0.52°C. Thus,

> Boiling point elevation = molality × (0.52°C)
>
> or
>
> $$\Delta t_b = \frac{\text{g solute per 1000 g of solvent}}{\text{molecular weight of solute}} \times (0.52°C)$$

3. The molecular weight of a non-volatile, non-electrolyte is 180. Calculate the boiling point of a solution that contains 360 g of solute in 500 g of water.

In 1000 g of water there will be:

$$360 \times \frac{1000}{500} = 720 \text{ g of solute}$$

$$\Delta t_b = \frac{\text{g solute per 1000 g of solvent}}{\text{molecular weight of solute}} \times (0.52°C)$$

$$= \frac{720}{180} \times 0.52°C$$

$$= 2.08°C$$

Since the boiling point of water is $100°C$, the solution will boil at $100°C + 2.08°C$ or $102.08°C$.

4. A solution of a non-electrolyte containing 50 g of solute in 500 g of naphthalene has a freezing point of $79.2°C$. The freezing point of pure naphthalene is $80.2°C$ and the molal freezing depression constant for naphthalene is $6.8°C$. Calculate the molecular weight of the solute.

In 1000 g of naphthalene, there will be

$$50 \times \frac{1000}{500} = 100 \text{ g of solute}$$

The depression of the freezing point is $80.2 - 79.2$ or $1.0°C$.

$$\Delta t_f = \frac{\text{g solute per 1000 g solvent}}{\text{molecular weight of solute}} \times (6.8°C.)$$

$$1.0°C = \frac{100}{\text{Molecular Wt.}} \times (6.8°C)$$

Molecular Weight = 680

PROBLEMS

(ANSWERS ON PAGE 156)

1. Calculate the mole fraction of ethylene glycol $C_2H_6O_2$ in a solution which contains 248 g of $C_2H_6O_2$ in 288 g of water.

2. Calculate the mole fraction of ethyl alcohol C_2H_6O in a solution which contains 500 g of ethyl alcohol in 500 g of water.

3. Calculate the vapor pressure of a solution that contains 90 g of glucose $C_6H_{12}O_6$ in 360 g of water at $18°C$. The vapor pressure of pure water at $18°C$ is 15.33 mm.

4. Calculate the vapor pressure of a solution that contains 100 g of glycerol $C_3H_8O_3$ in 100 g of water at $30°C$. The vapor pressure of pure water at $30°C$ is 31.51 mm.

5. A solution containing 8 g of a non-electrolyte dissolved in 350 g of water freezes at -0.82°C. Calculate the molecular weight of the solute.

6. A solution containing 20 g of a non-volatile non-electrolyte dissolved in 400 g of water freezes at -0.85°C. Calculate (a) the molecular weight of the solute and (b) the boiling point of the solution.

7. A solution containing 25 g of a non-volatile non-electrolyte dissolved in 200 g of water boils at 100.26°C. Calculate (a) the molecular weight of the solute and (b) freezing point of the solution.

8. A solution of a non-electrolyte containing 40 g of solute in 250 g of naphthalene has a freezing point of 78°C. The freezing point of pure naphthalene is 80.2°C, and the molal freezing point depression for naphthalene is 6.8°C. Calculate the molecular weight of the solute.

9. A solution of solute of 100 g of a non-electrolyte in 400 g of naphthalene has a freezing point of 76°C. Calculate the molecular weight of the solute.

10. Calculate the freezing point of a 20% solution of ethyl alcohol C_2H_6O in water.

11. What weight of ethyl alcohol C_2H_6O must be added to 4 liters of water so that the solution will freeze at -10°C?

12. What weight of methyl alcohol CH_4O must be added to 10 liters of water so that the solution will freeze at 0°F?

REACTIONS OF NORMAL SOLUTIONS

I. TITRATION

The use of solution of known concentration — a standard solution — for analyzing a solution of unknown concentration is known as titration. The volumes of the solutions used are accurately measured by means of burettes, which are graduated to 1/10 of a ml. A

102

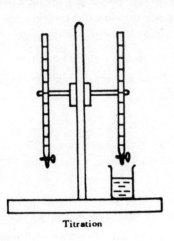

Titration

measured volume of acid is placed in a beaker, and a standard solution of base is added dropwise from the burette. The point at which the base exactly neutralizes the acid is known as the end-point and may be conveniently determined by means of an indicator.

An indicator is a dye stuff, which upon losing a proton, rearranges its bonding and changes in color. The indicator litmus, which is a very weak acid, is pink in color; when it becomes neutralized (loses a proton) it becomes a very weak base which is blue in color.

Thus when a few drops of litmus are added to an acid, the solution is pink. A standard base is added until the color is intermediate between pink and blue. (If one more drop of base were added, the solution would turn distinctly blue in color.) This point – the end-point – is then the point at which the base has neutralized the acid, and the volume of the base which has been added is read from the burette.

Other indicators which are commonly used are phenolphthalein, methyl orange, methyl red and congo red.

II. CALCULATION OF CONCENTRATIONS

One gram-equivalent of any acid will neutralize one gram-equivalent of any base; therefore any number of gram-equivalents of acid will exactly neutralize the same number of gram-equivalents of a base. Thus:

gram-equivalents of acid = gram-equivalents of base

Since normality is defined as the number of gram-equivalents per liter of solution; or:

$$N = \frac{\text{Number of gram-equivalents}}{\text{Number of liters}}$$

it follows that:

N × Number of liters = Number of gram-equivalents.

Then, since the number of equivalents of acid and base must be equal, the following expression is obtained.

(N of acid) (liters of acid) = (N of base) (liters of base)

or

(N of acid) (ml of acid) = (N of base) (ml of base)

or

$$N_a \times V_a = N_b \times V_b$$

If any three of these quantities are known, the fourth may readily be calculated.

EXAMPLES

1. What volume of 0.3 N HCl will be necessary to neutralize 30 ml of 0.2 N NaOH?

$$N_a \times V_a = N_b \times V_b$$

$$0.3 \times V_a = 0.2 \times 30 \text{ ml}$$

$$V_a = \frac{0.2 \times 30}{0.3} = 20 \text{ ml of acid}$$

2. What volume of 0.1 N H_2SO_4 will be required to neutralize a solution containing 10 g of $Ca(OH)_2$?

Note that the volume of the base solution is not stated, but $N_b \times V_b$ (liters) = number of gram equivalents of base.

Therefore $N_a \times V_a$ (liters) = gram equivalents of base

$Ca(OH)_2$ has equivalent weight $\frac{74}{2} = 37$ (Ca, valence +2)

10 g of $Ca(OH)_2$ is $\frac{10}{37}$ gram equivalents

$$0.1 \times V_a = \frac{10}{37}$$

$$V_a = \frac{10}{10 \times 37} = 2.7 \text{ liters of 0.1 N acid}$$

3. What weight of NiS will be precipitated when 100 ml of 0.2 N $Ni(NO_3)_2$ is saturated with H_2S?

gram equivalents of $Ni(NO_3)_2$ = gram equivalents of NiS

$$100 \text{ ml} = 0.1 \text{ liter}$$

gram equivalents of $Ni(NO_3)_2$ = $0.1 \times 0.2 = 0.02$

therefore, 0.02 gram equivalents of NiS are precipitated

equivalent weight of NiS = $\frac{91}{2}$ = 45.5   Ni has a valence of +2

1 gram equivalent of NiS = 45.5 g

0.02 gram equivalents = 0.02 × 45.5 = 0.91 g of NiS

4. What volume of hydrogen at STP will be liberated by adding excess magnesium to 200 ml of 0.25 N HCl?

gram equivalents of HCl = 0.2 × 0.25 = 0.05

therefore gram equivalents of hydrogen liberted = 0.05

1 gram equivalent of hydrogen = 1 g = 11.2 liters at STP

0.05 gram equivalents = 0.05 × 11.2 = 0.556 liters H_2

5. What weight of $BaCl_2$ is required to precipitate the $BaSO_4$ from 71 ml of 0.2 N H_2SO_4?

$$BaCl_2 + H_2SO_4 \longrightarrow BaSO_4 + 2HCl$$
1 mole   1 mole

1 mole of H_2SO_4 = 98 g = 2 gram equivalents (2 × 49 g)

then   1 mole of $BaCl_2$ = 208 g = 2 gram equivalents

because 1 gram equivalent of A reacts with 1 gram equivalent of B

71 ml of 0.2 N H_2SO_4 = 0.071 × 0.2 = 0.0142 gram equivalents

0.0142 gram equivalents of $BaCl_2$ are used

1 gram equivalent of $BaCl_2$ = 104 g

0.0142 gram equivalents = 0.0142 × 104 = 1.48 g of $BaCl_2$

In these problems the balanced equations help in determining any unknown equivalent weight.

Example: What volume of carbon dioxide at STP is liberated by the action of 250 ml of 0.1 N HCl on excess sodium carbonate?

$$Na_2CO_3 + 2HCl \longrightarrow 2NaCl + H_2O + CO_2$$
2 moles   1 mole

2 moles of HCl = 2 gram equivalents of HCl because the equivalent weight of HCl equals its formula weight.

2 equivalents of HCl will produce 2 equivalents of CO_2

therefore 1 mole of CO_2 = 2 equivalents of CO_2

At STP 1 mole of a gas occupies 22.4 liters. Therefore 1 gram equivalent of CO_2 occupies 11.2 liters at STP.

150 ml of 0.1 N HCl $= 0.25 \times 0.1 = 0.025$ gram equivalents

0.025 gram equivalents of CO_2 are produced

$0.025 \times 11.2 = 0.28$ liters

III. CALCULATIONS OF MOLAR SOLUTIONS

Although elements and compounds react in the proportion of their equivalents, one equivalent of A with one equivalent of B, this is not necessarily true for the ratio of moles. One mole of A will react with an amount of B determined by the balanced equation. Convert the volume of molar solution to a quantity in moles.

EXAMPLES

1. What volume of 0.4 M $AgNO_3$ solution will react with 100 ml of 0.25 M NaCl solution?

$$NaCl + AgNO_3 \longrightarrow NaNO_3 + AgCl$$
1 mole   1 mole

100 ml of 0.25 M NaCl contains $0.1 \times 0.25 = 0.025$ moles

then   0.025 moles of $AgNO_3$ are required

0.04 moles $AgNO_3$ are in 1 liter of 0.4 M solution

1 mole $AgNO_3$ in $\dfrac{1}{0.4}$ liter of 0.4 M solution

0.025 moles in $0.025 \times \dfrac{1}{0.4} = 0.0625$ liters (62.5 ml) of

$AgNO_3$ solution

62.5 ml of $AgNO_3$ solution required

2. 50 ml of 1.25 M Na_2CO_3 solution is reacted with 170 ml of a HCl solution. Calculate the molarity of the acid.

$$Na_2CO_3 + 2HCl \longrightarrow 2NaCl + H_2O + CO_2$$
1 mole   2 moles

50 ml of 1.25 M Na_2CO_3 contains $0.05 \times 1.25 = 0.0625$ moles

since 1 mole of the carbonate requires 2 moles of acid

0.0625 moles carbonate require 2×0.0625 moles acid

therefore 170 ml of acid solution contains 2×0.0625 moles

1 ml of acid contains $\dfrac{2 \times 0.0625}{170}$ moles

$$1000 \text{ ml (1 liter) contains } \frac{1000 \times 2 \times 0.0625}{170} \text{ moles}$$

$$= 0.735 \text{ moles}$$

The HCl solution is 0.735 molar

PROBLEMS

(ANSWERS ON PAGE 156)

1. 30 ml of 2 N base neutralize 90 ml of an acid. Calculate the normality of the acid.

2. 40 ml of 0.5 N acid neutralize 80 ml of a base. Calculate the normality of the base.

3. 25 ml of 0.4 acid neutralize 50 ml of $Ca(OH)_2$ solution. Calculate (a) the normality of the $Ca(OH)_2$ and (b) the number of grams of $Ca(OH)_2$ in 500 ml of solution.

4. In standardizing an H_2SO_4 solution, 25 ml of H_2SO_4 were required to neutralize 28 ml of 0.102 N NaOH. Calculate (a) the normality of the H_2SO_4 and (b) the number of grams of H_2SO_4 in 2 liters of solution.

5. What weight of CuS will be precipitated when 500 ml of 2N $CuSO_4$ solution is saturated with H_2S?

6. What weight of CdS will be precipitated when 300 ml of 1.25 N $Cd(NO_3)_2$ solution is saturated with H_2S?

7. What volume of CO_2 at STP will be formed when 250 ml of 0.4 N Na_2CO_3 solution are treated with excess H_2SO_4?

8. When 500 ml of H_2SO_4 were treated with excess zinc, 2.8ℓ of H_2 at 380 mm and $0°C$ were liberated. Calculate (a) the normality and (b) the molarity of the H_2SO_4 solution.

9. What volume of 0.8 N HCl is needed to liberate 18ℓ of CO_2 at 2 atm pressure from $CaCO_3$?

10. It was found that 20 ml of 0.4 N HCl solution were required to neutralize 1 g of an impure sample of magnesium oxide. Calculate the percentage purity of the MgO in the sample.

ELECTROCHEMISTRY

I. ELECTRICAL UNITS

1. Ampere

The ampere is the unit of current. One ampere (I) is that electric current which when passing through a solution of silver nitrate, will deposit 1.118 mg of Ag per second.

2. Coulomb

The coulomb is the unit of quantity of electricity. One coulomb is that quantity of electricity transferred by a current of 1 ampere in 1 second, or:

$$\text{coulombs} = \text{amperes} \times \text{seconds}$$

The charge on 1 electron is -1.602×10^{-19} coulombs

Therefore, 1 mole of electrons (6.02×10^{23} particles) carries a charge of $6.02 \times 10^{23} \times (-1.602 \times 10^{-19}) = 96,500$ coulombs

This quantity of charge, 96,500 coulombs is also called the faraday.

$$1 \text{ faraday} = 96,500 \text{ coulombs} = 1 \text{ mole of electron charge}$$

3. Ohm

The ohm is the unit of resistance. One ohm (R) is that resistance to an electric current which is equal to the resistance offered by a column of Hg 106.3 cm long and 1 square mm in cross section area at $0°C$.

4. Volt

The volt is the unit of potential difference. One volt (E) is that difference of potential which will cause a current of one ampere to flow through a resistance of 1 ohm.

5. Specific Resistance

The specific resistance is a constant which depends on the material of which the conductor is made and the temperature. It is expressed in ohm-cm.

$$\text{resistance (ohms)} = \text{Specific Resistance} \times \frac{\text{length in cm}}{\text{Cross section area in cm}^2}$$

6. Watt

The watt is the unit of power. One watt (P) is the power developed by 1 ampere in flowing through a potential difference of 1 volt or

$$P = EI$$

108

A kilowatt is equal to 1000 watts. A kilowatt-hour is the amount of energy furnished by a current whose power is 1 kilowatt flowing for 1 hour.

7. Ohm's Law

The current in a conductor is equal to the difference in potential across the conductor divided by the resistance of the conductor, or

$$\text{current (amps)} = \frac{\text{difference in potential (volts)}}{\text{resistance (ohms)}}$$

$$I = \frac{E}{R}$$

EXAMPLES

1. A current of 100 amperes was passed through an electrolytic cell for 40 seconds. Calculate the number of coulombs.

$$\text{coulombs} = \text{amperes} \times \text{seconds}$$
$$= 100 \text{ amps} \times 40 \text{ sec}$$
$$= 4000 \text{ coulombs}$$

2. Calculate the resistance at 20°C of a copper wire which has a length of 2000 cm and a cross section area of 0.4 cm². The specific resistance for copper at 20°C is 1.72×10^{-6} ohm-cm.

$$\text{resistance} = \text{specific resistance} \times \frac{\text{length}}{\text{cross section area}}$$
$$= 1.72 \times 10^{-6} \text{ ohm-cm} \times \frac{2000 \text{ cm}}{0.4 \text{ cm}^2}$$
$$= 8.6 \times 10^{-3} \text{ ohms}$$

3. Calculate the current that flows through a resistance of 20 ohms if the potential difference is 60 volts.

$$\text{amperes} = \frac{\text{volts}}{\text{ohms}}$$
$$= \frac{60}{20}$$
$$= 3 \text{ amperes}$$

4. Calculate the power generated by a current of 3 amperes if it flows through a resistance of 30 ohms. If the current flows for 100 hours, how many kilowatt hours are produced?

Since power is the product of volts and amperes, it is necessary to calculate the number of volts.

$$amperes = \frac{volts}{ohms}$$

$$volts = amperes \times ohms$$
$$= 3 \text{ amps} \times 30 \text{ ohms}$$
$$= 90 \text{ volts}$$

$$watts = volts \times amperes$$
$$= 90 \text{ volts} \times 3 \text{ amps}$$
$$= 270 \text{ watts}$$

$$270 \text{ watts} = \frac{270}{1000} = 0.27 \text{ kilowatts}$$

$$kilowatt\text{-}hours = kilowatts \times hours$$
$$= 0.27 \times 100$$
$$= 27 \text{ kilowatt-hours}$$

5. Calculate the resistance when a 4 ampere current produces a potential difference of 10 volts.

$$amperes = \frac{volts}{ohms}$$

$$ohms = \frac{volts}{amperes}$$
$$= \frac{10}{4}$$
$$= 2.5 \text{ ohms}$$

II. FARADAY'S LAW OF ELECTROLYSIS

1. The amount of an element formed or lost at an electrode is proportional to the quantity of charge that has flowed through the solution.

2. The amount of an element formed or lost at an electrode is directly proportional to the atomic weight of the element divided by the charge on the ion.

For example, if the same quantity of charge is passed through solutions containing respectively Ag^+, Cu^{2+}, and Al^{3+} ions, the quantity of each metal deposited will be in the ratio by weight of

$$\frac{108}{1} Ag \;:\; \frac{63.6}{2} Cu \;:\; \frac{27}{3} Al$$

The numbers 1, 2 and 3 are the valence numbers or charges on the ions, and the numbers 108, 63.6, and 27 are the atomic weights.

EXAMPLES

1. How many coulombs of electricity are required to deposit 5.4 g of silver on an electrode during the electrolysis of $AgNO_3$ solution?

At the cathode (negative electrode)

$$Ag^+ + e^- \longrightarrow Ag$$

1 mole of   1 mole of   1 mole of
    ions   electrons   atoms (deposited)

1 mole (108 g) of silver atoms are deposited when 1 mole of electron charge flows through the solution.

108 g Ag atoms are deposited by 96,500 coulombs of charge
                                                       flowing

5.4 g Ag deposited by $5.4 \times \dfrac{96500}{108}$ = 4825 coulombs

2. A current of 3 amperes is passed through a solution of $CuSO_4$ for 4 hours. Calculate the weight of copper deposited at the cathode.

Atomic Weight of Copper = 63.6

Reaction at the cathode

$$Cu^{2+} + 2e^- \longrightarrow Cu$$

1 mole of   2 moles of   1 mole of
    ions   electrons   atoms deposited

number of coulombs = 3 amperes $\times$ 4 $\times$ 60 $\times$ 60 seconds
                          = 43200

2 $\times$ 96500 coulombs of charge deposit 1 mole (63.6 g) of Cu atoms

43200 coulombs deposit $43200 \times \dfrac{63.6}{2 \times 96500}$ = 14.2 g Cu

3. A current of 3 amperes is passed through water for 2 hours. Calculate (a) the weight of oxygen liberated and (b) the volume of hydrogen liberated at STP. Atomic Weight O = 16

Reaction at anode

$$4OH^- - 4e^- \longrightarrow 2H_2O + O_2$$

                   4 moles of   1 mole of
                   electrons   oxygen molecules

Reaction at cathode

$$4H^+ + 4e^- \longrightarrow 2H_2$$

                   4 moles of   2 moles of
                   electrons   hydrogen gas

number of coulombs = 3 amperes × 2 hours × 3600 sec = 21,600

(a) 4 moles of electrons (4 × 96500 coulombs) liberate 1 mole (32 g) O_2

$$21600 \text{ coulombs liberate } 21600 \times \frac{32}{4 \times 96500}$$

$$= 1.79 \text{ g oxygen}$$

(b) 4 × 96500 coulombs liberate 2 moles H_2 gas (2 × 22.4 1 at STP)

$$21600 \text{ coulombs liberate } 21600 \times \frac{2 \times 22.4}{4 \times 96500} = 2.51 \text{ 1 at STP}$$

PROBLEMS

(ANSWERS ON PAGE 156)

1. Calculate the number of coulombs used when a current of 2 amperes flows for 20 minutes.

2. Calculate the number of coulombs used when a current of 3 amperes flows for 2 hours and 30 minutes.

3. The specific resistance of mercury is 98.5×10^{-6} ohm-cm at 50°C. Calculate the resistance at 50°C of a column of mercury 100 cm long, having a cross section area of 2.0 cm^2.

4. The specific resistance of a saturated solution of $CuSO_4$ is 29.4 ohm-cm. What is the resistance of this solution if electrodes of 200 cm^2 are placed 20 cm apart in the solution?

5. (a) What is the resistance of a wire that permits 2 amperes to flow when a voltage of 100 is applied? (b) Calculate the number of watts.

6. If a current of 2 amperes flows through a resistance of 55 ohms for 200 hours, calculate the number of kilowatt-hours.

7. What current is required to pass 2 Faradays per hours through an electroplating bath?

8. What current is required to pass 1000 coulombs per minute through an electrolytic cell?

9. How many hours will it take for a current of 500 amperes to form 100,000 liters of H_2 measured at standard conditions by the electrolysis of water?

10. A current liberates 44.8 liters of H_2 at 380 mm pressure and 0°C. Calculate (a) the number of liters of O_2 at STP formed by the same current, (b) the weight of the Ag formed by the same current.

11. In 1 hour and 30 minutes, a current of 26.7 amperes deposists 35.8 g of a metal. Calculate the equivalent weight of the metal. The valence = 3.

12. A current of 1000 amperes is used in a copper refining cell. If the current efficiency is 85%, calculate the number of pounds of Cu deposited in 24 hours.

EQUILIBRIUM

I. THE EQUILIBRIUM CONSTANT (Kc)

Consider the following general reversible reaction

$$A + B \underset{v_2}{\overset{v_1}{\rightleftharpoons}} C + D$$

From the law of mass action

$$v_1 = k_1 \, [A] \, [B]$$
$$v_2 = k_2 \, [C] \, [D]$$

Where v_1 and v_2 are the velocities of the forward and reverse reactions respectively; k_1 and k_2 are velocity constants; and the concentrations are given in moles per liter.

At equilibrium, $v_1 = v_2$

or $k_1[A] \, [B] \quad = k_2 \, [C] \, [D]$

or $\dfrac{[C] \, [D]}{[A] \, [B]} \quad = \dfrac{k_1}{k_2} = k_c$, the concentration equilibrium constant.

In the reaction

$$A + 2B \rightleftharpoons C + 2D$$

the equilibrium constant expression is

$$\frac{[C] \, [D]^2}{[A] \, [B]^2} = k_c$$

EXAMPLES

1. When 37.35 g of I_2 and 0.81 g of H_2 are heated in a 1-liter container at $445°C$, 36.10 g of HI are formed when equilibrium is attained. Calculate the equilibrium constant.

The equation for the reaction is

$$H_2 + I_2 \rightleftharpoons 2HI$$

The initial concentration in moles per liter is:

$$[H_2] = \frac{0.81 \text{ g}}{2 \text{ g/mole}} = 0.405 \text{ moles}$$

$$[I_2] = \frac{37.35 \text{ g}}{254 \text{ g/mole}} = 0.147 \text{ mole}$$

$$[HI] = \frac{36.10 \text{ g}}{128 \text{ g/mole}} = 0.282 \text{ mole}$$

The concentration in moles per liter at equilibrium is then calculated.

$$[HI] = 0.282 \text{ mole}$$

Since 2 moles of HI are formed from 1 mole of H_2 and 1 mole of I_2, the concentration of H_2 and I_2 at equilibrium will be the initial concentration minus 1/2 the amount necessary to form HI.

$$[H_2] = 0.405 - \frac{0.282}{2} = 0.264 \text{ mole}$$

$$[I_2] = 0.147 - \frac{0.282}{2} = 0.006 \text{ mole}$$

Now $K_c = \dfrac{[HI]^2}{[H_2][I_2]}$

$$K_c = \frac{[0.282]^2}{[0.264][0.006]} = 50.2$$

2. Calculate the number of grams of HI formed by mixing 508 g of I_2 and 6 g of H_2 in a 1-liter container, and allowing the mixture to attain equilibrium at 443°C. K_c for this temperature is 50.

$$H_2 + I_2 \rightleftharpoons 2HI$$

$$[H_2] = \frac{6 \text{ g}}{2 \text{ g/mole}} = 3 \text{ moles}$$

$$[I_2] = \frac{508 \text{ g}}{254 \text{ g/mole}} = 2 \text{ moles}$$

$$[HI] = x \text{ moles}$$

The concentration in moles per liter at equilibrium will be:

$$[H_2] = 3 - \frac{x}{2}$$

$$[I_2] = 2 - \frac{x}{2}$$

$$[HI] = x$$

Now: $K_c = \dfrac{[HI]^2}{[H_2][I_2]}$

$$50 = \frac{x^2}{\left(3 - \frac{x}{2}\right)\left(2 - \frac{x}{2}\right)} = \frac{4x^2}{(6-x)(4-x)}$$

Dividing by 4 and expanding

$$12.5 = \frac{x^2}{24 - 10x + x^2}$$

$$300 - 125x + 12.5x^2 = x^2$$

$$11.5x^2 - 125x + 300 = 0$$

$$x = \frac{-b \pm \sqrt{15,625 - 13,800}}{23}$$

$$x = \frac{125 \pm \sqrt{1825}}{23}$$

$$x = \frac{125 \pm 42.7}{23}$$

$$x = 7.28 \text{ or } 3.58 \text{ moles HI}$$

Obviously there cannot be formed 7.28 moles of HI, so this answer is disregarded.

$$3.58 \text{ moles} \times 128 \frac{g}{mole} = 457 \text{ g HI}$$

II. DISPLACEMENT OF EQUILIBRIUM

I. LeCHATELIER'S LAW

Whenever an outside force is brought up on a system in equilibrium, the equilbrium shifts in the direction so as to minimize the effect of of the applied force.

2. VAN'T HOFF'S LAW

Whenever the temperature of a system in equilibrium is raised, the equilibrium shifts in the direction that absorbs heat.

a. Changes in Pressure

When the pressure on a system in equilibrium is increased, the equilibrium shifts in the direction of the smaller volume.

$$2NO \quad + \quad O_2 \rightleftharpoons 2NO_2$$

2 volumes   1 volume   2 volumes

3 volumes

When NO combines with O_2 to form NO_2, there is a decrease in volume from 3 to 2. An increase in pressure will shift the equilibrium to the right and increase the yield of NO_2. If the volumes are the same on both sides of the equation, an increase or decrease in pressure has no effect on the equilibrium.

b. Changes in Temperature

The reaction

$$3H_2 + N_2 \rightleftharpoons 2NH_3 + 21,880 \text{ cal.}$$

is exothermic. When 3 moles of H_2 combine with 1 mole of N_2 to form 2 moles of NH_3, 21,880 calories are evolved. When 2 moles of NH_3 decompose to form 3 moles of H_2 and 1 mole of N_2, 21,880 calories are absorbed (endothermic).

When the temperature of this reaction is raised, the equilibrium is displaced to the left, since heat is absorbed as the reaction proceeds from right to left. If the temperature of this reaction is lowered, the equilibrium is displaced to the right.

c. Changes in Concentration

The equilibrium constant must remain for the same for any given temperature. In the reaction

$$PCl_5 \rightleftharpoons PCl_3 + Cl_2$$

the equilibrium constant expression is:

$$K_c = \frac{[PCl_3] \, [Cl_2]}{[PCl_5]}$$

If the Cl_2 concentration is increased, the PCl_3 concentration must decrease and the PCl_5 concentration must increase in order for the constant to remain the same. The equilibrium shifts to the left. If the PCl_5 concentration is increased, the concentrations of PCl_3 and Cl_2 must increase in order for the constant to remain the same. The equilibrium shifts to the right.

116

d. Catalysts

A catalyst does not effect the point of equilibrium. The rates of both forward and reverse reactions are affected equally by catalysts. A catalyst affects the speed with which equilibrium is attained, but the equilibrium concentrations are not affected.

PROBLEMS

(ANSWERS ON PAGE 157)

1. Write the equilibrium constant expression for:

   (a) $N_2 + 3H_2 \rightleftharpoons 2NH_3$

   (b) $N_2 + O_2 \rightleftharpoons 2NO$

   (c) $PCl_5 \rightleftharpoons PCl_3 + Cl_2$

   (d) $2CO + O_2 \rightleftharpoons 2CO_2$

   (e) $4HCl + O_2 \rightleftharpoons 2H_2O + 2Cl_2$

2. In the reaction $CO_{(g)} + 2H_{2(g)} \rightleftharpoons CH_3OH_{(g)} + 24{,}200$ cal. State what happens to the equilibrium if:

   (a) The CO concentration is increased.

   (b) The H_2 concentration is decreased.

   (c) The CH_3OH concentration is decreased.

   (d) The CH_3OH concentration is increased.

   (e) The pressure on the system is increased.

   (f) The pressure on the system is decreased.

   (g) The temperature of the system is increased.

   (h) The temperature of the system is decreased.

3. The reaction $N_{2(g)} + O_{2(g)} \rightleftharpoons 2NO_{(g)}$ is endothermic. State what happens to the equilibrium if:

   (a) The pressure is increased.

   (b) The pressure is decreased.

   (c) The temperature is lowered.

   (d) The temperature is raised.

   (e) The NO is removed as it is formed.

   (f) Presence of a catalyst.

4. In the reaction $CaO_{(s)} + CO_{2(g)} \rightleftharpoons CaCO_{3(s)} + 43,100$ cal.
   State what happens to the equilibrium if:

   (a) The pressure is increased.

   (b) The pressure is decreased.

   (c) The temperature is raised.

   (d) The CaO concentration is decreased.

   (e) The CO_2 concentration is increased.

5. When 112.05 g of I_2 and 2.43 of H_2 are heated in a 1-liter container at 445°C, 108.30 g of HI are formed when equilibrium is reached. Calculate the equilibrium constant.

6. When 242 g of PCl_5 are heated in a 1-liter container at 300°C, 88 g of PCl_3 and 45.5 g of Cl_2 are formed when equilibrium is reached. Calculate the equilibrium constant.

7. Calculate the number of grams of PCl_3 formed at equilibrium when 417 g of PCl_5 are placed in a 1-liter container and heated to 250°C. K_c for this temperature is 0.041.

8. Calculate the number of grams of I_2 left at equilibrium when 762 g of I_2 and 3 g of H_2 are mixed in a 1-liter container and heated to 443°C. K_c for this temperature is 50.

IONIC EQUILIBRIUM AND COMMON ION

I. IONIZATION CONSTANT

The principles of equilibrium and the law of mass action pertain also to solution of weak electrolytes. When NH_4OH is dissolved in water, the ammonium hydroxide molecules are in equilibrium with ammonium ions and hydroxide ions.

$$NH_4OH \rightleftharpoons NH_4^+ + OH^-$$

By application of the laws of chemical equilibrium, it is found that

$$\frac{\text{Conc. NH}_4^+ \times \text{conc. OH}^-}{\text{Conc. NH}_4\text{OH}} = \text{a constant}$$

or $\quad \dfrac{[\text{NH}_4^+][\text{OH}^-]}{[\text{NH}_4\text{OH}]} = K_i \text{ (Ionization Constant)}$

The concentrations are always given in moles per liter.

EXAMPLES

1. A 0.1 M solution of NH_4OH is 1.34% ionized. Calculate the ionization constant.

$$\underset{\text{NH}_4\text{OH}}{\overset{0.1}{}} \rightleftharpoons \overset{1.34\%}{\text{NH}_4^+ + \text{OH}^-}$$

The NH_4^+ concentration must equal the OH^- concentration, and both are equal to the concentration of NH_4OH times the fraction of ionization.

$$[\text{NH}_4^+] = [\text{OH}^-] = 0.1 \frac{\text{mole}}{\ell} \times 0.0134 = 0.00134 \frac{\text{mole}}{\ell}$$

Since 1.34% = 0.0134

The NH_4OH concentration at equilibrium = the initial concentration minus the amount ionized.

$$[\text{NH}_4\text{OH}] = 0.1 \frac{\text{mole}}{\ell} - 0.00134 \frac{\text{mole}}{\ell} = 0.09866 \frac{\text{mole}}{\ell}$$

$$k_i = \frac{[\text{NH}_4^+][\text{OH}^-]}{[\text{NH}_4\text{OH}]}$$

$$= \frac{[0.00134][0.00134]}{[0.09866]}$$

$$= 1.8 \times 10^{-5}$$

2. Calculate the concentration in moles per liter of an acetic acid solution which is 1.36% ionized. K_i for HAc is 1.85×10^{-5}.

$$\text{HAc} \rightleftharpoons \text{H}^+ + \text{Ac}^-$$

Let X = concentration in moles per liter of HAc solution.

Then $[\text{H}^+] = [\text{Ac}^-] = 0.0136 \times \text{X}$

Since 1.36% = 0.0136

The HAc concentration at equilibrium = the initial concentration minus the amount ionized.

$$[\text{HAc}] = \text{X} - 0.0136\text{X}$$

In this expression, 0.0136X will be so small as compared to X that the [HAc] will be practically equal to X. A number such as this may be dropped only when it is added to or subtracted from a much larger number.

$$K_i = \frac{[H^+][Ac^-]}{[HAc]}$$

$$1.85 \times 10^{-5} = \frac{[0.0136X][0.0136X]}{[X-0.0136X]}$$

$$1.85 \times 10^{-5}X = (1.36 \times 10^{-2})^2 X^2$$

$$1.85 \times 10^{-5} = 1.85 \times 10^{-4} X$$

$$\frac{1.85 \times 10^{-5}}{1.85 \times 10^{-4}} = X$$

$$1 \times 10^{-1} = X$$

$$0.1 M = X$$

3. The ionization constant for HCN = 2.1×10^{-9}. Calculate the degree of ionization of a 0.1 M solution.

$$HCN \rightleftharpoons H^+ + CN^-$$

Let X = degree of ionization

$$[H^+] = [CN^-] = 0.1 X$$

$$[HCN] = 0.1 - 0.1 X$$

$$K_i = \frac{[H^+][CN^-]}{[HCN]}$$

$$2.1 + 10^{-9} = \frac{[0.1X][0.1X]}{[0.1 - 0.1X]}$$

Since 0.1 X will be small as compared to 0.1, it may be dropped without causing a serious error.

$$2.1 \times 10^{-9} = \frac{0.01X^2}{0.1}$$

$$0.01X^2 = 2.1 \times 10^{-10}$$

$$X^2 = 2.1 \times 10^{-8}$$

$$X = 1.4 \times 10^{-4} \text{ or } 0.014\%$$

The principles of chemical equilibrium cannot be applied to solutions of strong electrolytes because strong electrolytes are completely ionized at all concentrations. In a 0.01 molar solution of

120

NaOH, the concentration of Na$^+$ and OH are both 0.01 M and that of the undissociated NaOH is zero. The ionization constant expression becomes

$$K_i = \frac{[Na^+][OH^-]}{[NaOH]} = \frac{[0.01][0.01]}{0} = \text{meaningless.}$$

II. IONIZATION OF WATER

Water is a very weak acid and the ionization may be represented as:

$$H_2O + H_2O \rightleftharpoons H_3O^+ + OH^-$$

This equation may be simplified by neglecting hydration of the proton.

$$H_2O \rightleftharpoons H^+ + OH^-$$

The ionization constant expression is:

$$K_i = \frac{[H^+][OH^-]}{[H_2O]}$$

The fraction of ionization of water is so small, that the concentration of the undissociated molecules may be considered constant, and may be absorbed in the ionization constant.

$$K_i[H_2O] = [H^+][OH^-]$$

In pure water and in dilute aqueous solutions, the product of $[H^+]$ and $[OH^-]$ is a constant, 1×10^{-14} mole per liter. It is designated as K_w and is called the ion product of water.

$$K_w = [H^+][OH^-] = 1 \times 10^{-14}$$

If either the $[H^+]$ or $[OH^-]$ is known, the other may be calculated.

EXAMPLE

1. The $[H^+]$ of a dilute acid is 1×10^{-3} mole per liter. Calculate the $[OH^-]$.

$$[H^+][OH^-] = 1 \times 10^{-14}$$

$$[OH^-] = \frac{1 \times 10^{-14}}{[H^+]}$$

$$= \frac{1 \times 10^{-14}}{1 \times 10^{-3}}$$

$$[OH^-] = 1 \times 10^{-11} \text{ mole per liter}$$

III. COMMON ION EFFECT

Ionic equilibrium, just as all systems in equilibrium, may be displaced by a change in concentration in accord with LeChatelier's law. Let us examine the effect of adding solid ammonium chloride to a solution of NH_4OH.

$$NH_4OH \rightleftharpoons NH_4^+ + OH^-$$

$$K_i = \frac{[NH_4^+][OH^-]}{[NH_4OH]}$$

The NH_4Cl is a strong electrolyte, and is completely ionized at all concentrations.

$$NH_4Cl \longrightarrow NH_4^+ + Cl^-$$

The substance which is common to both equations is the ammonium ion (common ion), and thus the solution becomes more concentrated with respect to NH_4^+. In order for K_i to remain constant, the equilibrium must shift to the left, causing a decrease in the OH^- concentration and an increase in the NH_4OH concentration. The chloride ions will not have an appreciable effect on this system in equilibrium.

EXAMPLE

1. Calculate the OH^- concentration of 0.1M NH_4OH solution in which is dissolved 0.2 mole of NH_4Cl. K_i for NH_4OH is 1.8×10^{-5}.

$$NH_4OH \rightleftharpoons NH_4^+ + OH^-$$

$$K_i = \frac{[NH_4^+][OH^-]}{[NH_4OH]}$$

Since the NH_4OH is only very slightly ionized, it may be assumed that all of the NH_4^+ concentration comes from the NH_4Cl and that the NH_4OH concentration is essentially equal to the molarity of the NH_4OH.

$$K_i = \frac{[NH_4^+][OH^-]}{[NH_4OH]}$$

$$1.8 \times 10^{-5} = \frac{[0.2][OH^-]}{[0.1]}$$

$$[OH^-] = \frac{[1.8 \times 10^{-5}][0.1]}{[0.2]}$$

$$[OH^-] = 9 \times 10^{-6} \text{ mole/liter}$$

IV. PROBLEMS

(ANSWERS ON PAGE 158)

1. A 0.1M solution of acetic acid is 1.35% ionized.
   Calculate the ionization constant for acetic acid.

2. A 0.1M solution of benzoic acid is 0.026% ionized.
   Calculate the ionization constant of benzoic acid.

   $$C_6H_5COOH \rightleftharpoons C_6H_5COO^- + H^+$$

3. A solution of formic acid is 5% ionized. Calculate the molarity of this solution if the ionization constant for formic acid is 2.15×10^{-4}.

   $$HCOOH \rightleftharpoons HCOO^- + H^+$$

4. A solution of HCN is 0.014% ionized. Calculate the molarity of this solution if the ionization constant for HCN is 2.1×10^{-9}.

5. The ionization constant for NH_4OH is 1.8×10^{-5}. Calculate the percentage ionization of (a) 1.0M solution, (b) 0.1M solution.

6. The ionization constant for formic acid is 2.15×10^{-4}. Calculate the $[H^+]$ and $[OH^-]$ of a 2M solution of HCOOH.

7. The ionization constant for methyl ammonium hydroxide is 5.0×10^{-4}. Calculate the $[H^+]$ and $[OH^-]$ of a 0.1M solution of this base:

   $$CH_3NH_3OH \rightleftharpoons CH_3NH_3^+ + OH^-.$$

8. Calculate the $[OH^-]$ concentration of 0.1M NH_4OH solution which has been made 0.8M with respect to $[NH_4^+]$.

9. Calculate the $[H^+]$ concentration of 0.1M HAc solution in one ℓ of which is dissolved 0.4 mole of solid NaAc. K_i for HAc is 1.85×10^{-5}. Neglect all volume changes.

10. Calculate the $[H^+]$ concentration in 200 ml of 0.1M HCN solution to which has been added 10 g of solid NaCN. K_i for HCN is

    2.1×10^{-9}. Neglect all volume changes.

HYDROGEN ION INDEX

I. NEUTRAL, ACIDIC AND BASIC SOLUTIONS

Pure water is neutral because it has the concentrations of hydrogen ions and hydroxyl ions equal.

At 25°C pure water has $[H^+] = [OH^-] = 10^{-7}$ moles/liter

Therefore a neutral solution is defined as one in which the hydrogen ion concentration equals the hydroxyl ion concentration.

An acid solution has more H^+ than OH^- and has a $[H^+]$ more than 10^{-7} moles/liter, as 1×10^{-5}, 2.4×10^{-3} etc.

Basic solutions have more OH^- than H^+ and the $[H^+]$ is less than 10^{-7} moles/liter, as 1×10^{-8}, 1.3×10^{-12} etc.

Ion Product Constant

$[H^+] \times [OH^-]$ for pure water at 25°C = $10^{-7} \times 10^{-7} = 10^{-14}$ moles^2/litre^2

This is called the ion product. Any dilute water solution of acid, base or salt is considered to have $[H^+] \times [OH^-] = 10^{-14}$

EXAMPLE

What is the hydroxyl ion concentration of a solution if the hydrogen ion concentration is 1×10^{-4}? Is the solution acidic or basic?

$$[H^+] \times [OH^-] = 10^{-14} \text{ (moles/liter)}^2$$
$$10^{-4} \times [OH^-] = 10^{-14}$$
$$[OH^-] = \frac{10^{-14}}{10^{-4}} = 10^{-10} \text{ moles/liter}$$

Since the $[H^+] = 10^{-4}$ is greater than 10^{-7} the solution is acidic.

II. THE pH SCALE

Instead of denoting $[H^+]$ by the above method, which involves extremely small numbers, the pH scale is commonly used. The pH of a solution is defined as the logarithm of the reciprocal of the hydrogen ion concentration.

$$pH = \log \frac{1}{[H^+]} \text{ where the } [H^+] \text{ is expressed in moles per liter}$$

The $[H^+]$ in pure water is 1×10^{-7} mole per liter. The pH of pure water is:

$$pH = \log \frac{1}{[H^+]}$$

$$= \log \frac{1}{1 \times 10^{-7}}$$

$$= \log 1 \times 10^7$$

$$= 7$$

The pH of a neutral solution is then 7. Acidic solutions have a pH less than 7 and alkaline solutions have a pH greater than 7.

EXAMPLES

1. The $[H^+]$ of a solution is 5×10^{-4} mole per liter. Calculate the pH.

$$pH = \log \frac{1}{[H^+]}$$

$$= \frac{1}{\log 5 \times 10^{-4}}$$

$$= \log 0.2 \times 10^4$$

$$= \log 2 \times 10^3$$

$$= 3 + \log 2$$

$$= 3 + 0.30$$

$$= 3.30$$

2. Calculate the $[H^+]$ of a solution whose pH is 8.3.

$$pH = \log \frac{1}{[H^+]}$$

$$8.3 = \log \frac{1}{[H^+]}$$

Taking the antilogarithm of both sides:

$$2 \times 10^8 = \frac{1}{[H^+]}$$

$$[H^+] = \frac{1}{2 \times 10^8}$$

$$= 0.5 \times 10^{-8}$$

$$= 5 \times 10^{-9} \frac{mole}{\ell}$$

3. Calculate the pH of 0.001M HCl

$$HCl \longrightarrow H^+ + Cl^-$$

Since HCl is a strong electrolyte and is 100% ionized, the $[H^+]$ is 1×10^{-3} mole/liter. The pH is:

$$pH = \log \frac{1}{1 \times 10^{-3}}$$

$$= \log 1 \times 10^{-3}$$

$$= 3$$

4. Calculate the pH of 0.01M NaOH.

$$NaOH \longrightarrow Na^+ + OH^-$$

Since NaOH is a strong electrolyte and is 100% ionized, the $[OH^-]$ is 1×10^{-2} mole/liter.

Then, since $[H^+][OH^-] = 1 \times 10^{-14}$

$$[H^+] = \frac{1 \times 10^{-14}}{1 \times 10^{-2}} = 1 \times 10^{-12} \frac{mole}{\ell}$$

The pH is:

$$pH = \log \frac{1}{1 \times 10^{-12}}$$

$$= \log 1 \times 10^{12}$$

$$= 12$$

5. Calculate the pH of 0.025M monoprotic acid which is 4% ionized.

$$HA \rightleftharpoons H^+ + A^-$$

The $[H^+]$ of this solution is:

$$0.025 \frac{mole}{\ell} \times 0.04 = 0.001 \text{ mole per liter.}$$

The pH is:

$$pH = \log \frac{1}{[H^+]}$$

$$pH = \log \frac{1}{1 \times 10^{-3}}$$

$$= \log 1 \times 10^3$$

$$= 3$$

126

6. Calculate the pH of 0.002M base which is 5% ionized.

$$MOH \rightleftharpoons M^+ + OH^-$$

The [OH⁻] of this solution is:

$$0.002 \frac{mole}{\ell} \times 0.05 = 0.0001 \text{ mole per liter}$$

The [H⁺] is:

$$[H^+] = \frac{1 \times 10^{-14}}{1 \times 10^4} = 1 \times 10^{-10} \text{ mole per liter.}$$

$$pH = \log \frac{1}{[H^+]}$$

$$= \log \frac{1}{1 \times 10^{-10}}$$

$$= \log 1 \times 10^{10}$$

$$= 10$$

7. Calculate the pH of 1 liter of 0.1 M HAc solution in which is dissolved 0.5 mole of solid NaAc. K_i for HAc is 1.85×10^{-5}.

$$HAc \rightleftharpoons H^+ + Ac^-$$

$$K_i = \frac{[H^+] [Ac^-]}{[HAc]}$$

The [H⁺] must first be calculated. It may be assumed that all of the [Ac⁻] is derived from the NaAc, and that the [HAc] is essentially equal to the initial molarity of the HAc.

$$1.85 \times 10^{-5} = \frac{[H^+] [0.5]}{[0.1]}$$

$$[H^+] = \frac{1.85 \times 10^{-6}}{0.5} = 3.7 \times 10^{-6} \text{ mole per liter}$$

$$pH = \log \frac{1}{[H^+]}$$

$$= \log \frac{1}{3.7 \times 10^{-6}}$$

$$= \log 2.7 \times 10^5$$

$$= 5 + \log 2.7$$

$$= 5.43$$

PROBLEMS
(ANSWERS ON PAGE 157)

1. Convert the following $[H^+]$ to pH values: (a) 1×10^{-6}
   (b) 1×10^{-12} (c) 1.25×10^{-3} (d) 3.42×10^{-9} (e) 6.0×10^{-4}

2. Calculate the $[H^+]$ and $[OH^-]$ of solutions having the following
   pH value (a) 6 (b) 12 (c) 2.3 (d) 10.6 (e) 4.8.

3. Calculate the pH of each of the following solutions:
   (a) 0.01 M HCl, (b) 0.001 M HBr, (c) 0.002 M HCl,
   (d) 0.005 M HCl, (e) 0.0004 M HNO_3.

4. Calculate the pH of each of the following solutions:
   (a) 0.0001 M KOH, (b) 0.001 M NaOH, (c) 0.002 M LiOH,
   (d) 0.005 M NaOH, (e) 0.035 M KOH.

5. Calculate the pH of each of the following solutions:
   (a) 0.005 N acid which is 2% ionized,
   (b) 0.04 N acid which is 2.5% ionized,
   (c) 0.002 N acid which is 3% ionized,
   (d) 0.6 N acid which is 2% ionized.

SOLUBILITY PRODUCTS

I. SLIGHTLY SOLUBLE SALTS

When a salt which is slightly soluble is added to water, an equilibrium
is established between the undissolved solute and the solute present
in the solution. The solution is then said to be a saturated solution.
When AgBr, which is only slightly soluble, is added to water, the solid
AgBr is in equilibrium with Ag^+ and Br^-.

$$AgBr \rightleftharpoons Ag^+ + Br^-$$

The equilibrium constant expression is:

$$K_{eq} = \frac{[Ag^+][Br^-]}{[AgBr]}$$

Since the AgBr is present as a solid, its concentration is constant and
may be absorbed in the equilibrium constant.

$$K_{eq}[AgBr] = [Ag^+][Br^-]$$

The constant so obtained is known as the solubility product constant and is denoted as K_{sp}.

$$K_{sp} \text{ for AgBr} = [Ag^+][Br^-]$$

Concentrations are always given in moles per liter.

$$K_{sp} \text{ for Ag}_2\text{CrO}_4 = [Ag^+]^2[CrO_4^{--}]$$

$$K_{sp} \text{ for Al(OH)}_3 = [Al^{+++}][OH^-]^3$$

II. CALCULATION OF SOLUBILITY PRODUCT CONSTANTS

EXAMPLES

1. The solubility of AgBr is 7.9×10^{-5} g per liter of water. Calculate the solubility product constant. The solubility of AgBr in moles per liter is

$$\frac{7.9 \times 10^{-5} \text{ g}/\ell}{188 \text{ g/mole}} = 4.2 \times 10^{-7} \text{ mole per liter}$$

$$AgBr \rightleftharpoons Ag^+ + Br^-$$

For every mole of dissolved AgBr, there are 1 mole of Ag^+ and 1 mole of Br^-. The concentration of Ag^+ and Br^- are both equal to 4.2×10^{-7}.

$$\begin{aligned} K_{sp} \text{ for AgBr} &= [Ag^+][Br^-] \\ &= [4.2 \times 10^{-7}][4.2 \times 10^{-7}] \\ &= 17.64 \times 10^{-14} \\ &= 1.764 \times 10^{-13} \end{aligned}$$

2. The solubility of $Ag_2Cr_2O_7$ is 8.3×10^{-3} g per 100 g of water. Calculate K_{sp} for $Ag_2Cr_2O_7$.

The solubility of $Ag_2Cr_2O_7$ in one liter of water is:

$$8.3 \times 10^{-3} \text{ g} \times \frac{1000}{100} = 8.3 \times 10^{-2} \frac{\text{g}}{\ell}$$

The solubility in moles per liter is:

$$\frac{8.3 \times 10^{-2} \text{ g}/\ell}{432 \text{ g/mole}} = 1.92 \times 10^{-4} \text{ mole per liter.}$$

One mole of dissolved $Ag_2Cr_2O_7$ yields 2 moles of Ag^+ and 1 mole of $Cr_2O_7^=$.

$$Ag_2Cr_2O_7 \rightleftharpoons 2Ag^+ + Cr_2O_7^=.$$

$$[Ag^+] = 2 \times 1.92 \times 10^{-4} = 3.84 \times 10^{-4} \frac{mole}{\ell}$$

$$[Cr_2O_7^=] = 1.92 \times 10^{-4} \frac{mole}{\ell}$$

$$
\begin{aligned}
K_{sp} \text{ for } Ag_2Cr_2O_7 &= [Ag^+]^2[Cr_2O_7^=] \\
&= [3.84 \times 10^{-4}]^2[1.92 \times 10^{-4}] \\
&= [1.47 \times 10^{-7}][1.92 \times 10^{-4}] \\
&= 2.83 \times 10^{-11}
\end{aligned}
$$

III. CALCULATION OF SOLUBILITY FROM Ksp

EXAMPLES

1. K_{sp} for $PbCrO_4$ is 2×10^{-14}. Calculate the solubility of $PbCrO_4$ in $\frac{g}{\ell}$

$$PbCrO_4 \rightleftharpoons Pb^{++} + CrO_4^=$$

Let x = the concentration of Pb^{++} and $CrO_4^=$ in moles per liter.

$$
\begin{aligned}
K_{sp} \text{ for } PbCrO_4 &= [Pb^{++}][CrO_4^=] \\
2 \times 10^{-14} &= [x][x] \\
x^2 &= 2 \times 10^{-14} \\
x &= 1.41 \times 10^{-7} \frac{mole}{\ell}
\end{aligned}
$$

Multiplying by the molecular weight of $PbCrO_4$.

$$1.41 \times 10^{-7} \frac{mole}{\ell} \times 323 \frac{g}{mole} = 456 \times 10^{-5} \frac{g}{\ell}$$

2. K_{sp} for PbI_2 is 1.39×10^{-8} at $25°C$. Calculate the solubility of PbI_2 in gram/liter at $25°C$.

$$PbI_2 \rightleftharpoons Pb^{++} + 2I^-$$

Let x = $[Pb^{++}]$ in $\frac{moles}{\ell}$

$$2x = [I^-]$$

$$K_{sp} \text{ for } PbI_2 = [Pb^{++}] [I^-]^2$$

$$1.39 \times 10^{-8} = [x] [2x]^2$$

$$4x^3 = 1.39 \times 10^{-8}$$

$$x^3 = 3.47 \times 10^{-9}$$

$$x = 1.52 \times 10^{-3} \frac{mole}{\ell}$$

$$1.52 \times 10^{-3} \frac{mole}{\ell} \times 461 \frac{g}{mole} = 7 \times 10^{-1} \frac{g}{\ell}$$

IV. OTHER APPLICATIONS OF THE SOLUBILITY PRODUCT PRINCIPLE

EXAMPLES

1. What will be the concentration of Ag^+ left in solution if enough HBr is added to a solution of $AgNO_3$ to make the final Br^- concentration 0.1 molar?

$$K_{sp} \text{ for } AgBr = 7.7 \times 10^{-13}$$

$$[Ag^+] [Br^-] = 7.7 \times 10^{-13}$$

$$[Ag^+] [0.1] = 7.7 \times 10^{-13}$$

$$[Ag^+] = \frac{7.7 \times 10^{-13}}{0.1}$$

$$[Ag^+] = 7.7 \times 10^{-12} \frac{mole}{\ell}$$

2. A solution contains 0.001 mole CN^- and 0.01 mole Br^-. If Ag^+ is added dropwise to this solution, will AgBr or AgCN be precipitated first?

Ag^+ necessary to precipitate AgCN.

$$K_{sp} \text{ for } AgCN = 2.2 \times 10^{-12}$$

$$[Ag^+] [CN^-] = 2.2 \times 10^{-12}$$

$$[Ag^+] [0.001] = 2.2 \times 10^{-12}$$

$$[Ag^+] = 2.2 \times 10^{-9}$$

Ag^+ necessary to precipitate AgBr.

$$K_{sp} \text{ for AgBr} = 7.7 \times 10^{-13}$$
$$[Ag^+][Br^-] = 7.7 \times 10^{-13}$$
$$[Ag^+][0.01] = 7.7 \times 10^{-13}$$
$$[Ag^+] = 7.7 \times 10^{-11}$$

Since a smaller concentration of Ag^+ is necessary to cause precipitation of AgBr than AgCN, AgBr will precipitate first.

PROBLEMS

(ANSWERS ON PAGE 158)

1. Write the solubility product constant expression for each of the following compounds. (a) AgCl (b) $PbCO_3$ (c) Ag_2CrO_4 (d) Ag_2CO_3 (e) MgF_2 (f) SrF_2 (g) $Fe(OH)_3$.

2. Calculate K_{sp} for each of the following compounds. The solubilities are given in moles per liter. (a) $PbCl_2$, 6.5×10^{-2} (b) $BaSO_4$, 7.42×10^{-5} (c) CuI, 4.09×10^{-5} (d) Ag_2S, 8.08×10^{-6} (e) Ag_2CrO_4, 4.3×10^{-3}.

3. Calculate K_{sp} for each of the following compounds. The solubilities are given g/100 g of water. (a) PbS, 1×10^{-4} (b) AgCl, 1.52×10^{-4} (c) $MgCO_3$, 1.06×10^{-2} (d) CaF_2, 3.7×10^{-3}.

4. Calculate the solubility of each of the following compounds in g/ℓ from the K_{sp}. (a) AgCl, $K_{sp} = 1.6 \times 10^{-10}$ (b) MnS, $K_{sp} = 1.4 \times 10^{-15}$ (c) CdS, $K_{sp} = 3.6 \times 10^{-29}$ (d) BaF_2, $K_{sp} = 1.7 \times 10^{-6}$.

5. Determine the concentration of Ba^{++} left in solution if enough H_2SO_4 is added to a solution of $BaCl_2$ to make the final $SO_4^=$ concentration 0.01 molar. K_{sp} $BaSO_4 = 1.1 \times 10^{-10}$.

6. Determine the concentration of Ca^{++} left in solution if enough HF is added to a solution of $Ca(NO_3)_2$ to make the final F^- concentration 0.2 molar. $K_{sp} CaF_2 = 4.0 \times 10^{-11}$.

7. A solution contains 0.01 mole of $CrO_4^=$ and 0.1 mole of $SO_4^=$. If Ba^{++} is added dropwise to this solution, will $BaCrO_4$ or $BaSO_4$ be precipitated first? $K_{sp} BaSO_4 = 1.1 \times 10^{-10}$, $K_{sp} BaCrO_4 = 2.4 \times 10^{-10}$.

8. A solution contains 0.01 mole of $CO_3^=$ and 0.01 mole $SO_4^=$. If Pb^{++} is added to this solution will $PbCO_3$, or $PbSO_4$ be precipitated first? $K_{sp} PbCO_3 = 4.0 \times 10^{-14}$, $K_{sp} PbSO_4 = 1.1 \times 10^{-8}$.

9. How many grams of silver chloride will dissolve in 100 ml of 0.1 M sodium chloride solution? $K_{sp} AgCl = 1.6 \times 10^{-10}$

10. How many grams of silver bromide will dissolve in 1 liter of 0.2 M $CaBr_2$ solution? $K_{sp} AgBr = 7.7 \times 10^{-13}$.

THERMOCHEMISTRY

I. DEFINITIONS

A. Heat Units

The quantity of heat is commonly measured by means of 3 units.

1. Calories

One calorie (cal.) is the amount of heat necessary to raise the temperature of one gram of water one degree centigrade. For very accurate work it is defined as the amount of heat required to raise the temperature of one gram of water from $15°C$ to $16°C$.

2. Kilocalories

One Kilocalorie (kcal) = 1000 calories

3. British Thermal Units

One British thermal unit (Btu) is the amount of heat necessary to raise the temperature of one pound of water one degree fahrenheit.

1 Btu = 252 cal.

B. Specific Heat

The specific heat of a substance is the number of calories required to raise the temperature of one gram of the substance one degree centigrade. Specific heat is expressed as calories per gram per degree C. The specific heat of water is $1 \text{ cal/g}°C$; ice, $0.5 \text{ cal/g}°C$; steam, $0.48 \text{ cal/g}°C$.

The number of calories that are gained or lost by a substance will be equal to the mass in grams × specific heat × the temperature change in °C.

EXAMPLE

1. How many calories are required to heat 25 g of water from $20°C$ to $30°C$?

$$\text{Cal} = \text{mass} \times \text{sp.ht} \times \text{temp. change}$$
$$= 25 \text{ g} \times 1 \text{ cal/g}^\circ\text{C} \times 10^\circ\text{C}.$$
$$= 250 \text{ cal}.$$

2. When 400 g of a metal at 100°C were placed in 80 g of water at 50°C, the system attained temperature equilibrium at 90°C. Calculate the specific heat of the metal.

Heat lost by metal = heat gained by water

mass $\times$ sp.ht $\times$ temp. change = mass $\times$ sp.ht $\times$ temp. change

$$400 \times \text{sp.ht} \times (100\text{-}90) = 80 \times 1 \times (90\text{-}50)$$

$$\text{sp. ht} = \frac{80 \times 40}{400 \times 10}$$

$$= 0.8 \text{ cal/g}^\circ\text{C}$$

C. Heat of Fusion

The heat of fusion of a solid is the number of calories necessary to change 1 gram of a substance from a solid to a liquid without changing its temperature. The heat of fusion of ice is 80 cal/g.

EXAMPLE

1. How many calories are necessary to change 100 g of ice at 0°C to water at 0°C?

Since the heat of fusion of ice is 80 cal/g the number of calories necessary will be:

$$80 \text{ cal/g} \times 100 \text{ g} = 8000 \text{ cal}.$$

D. Heat of Vaporization

The heat of vaporization of a liquid is the number of calories necessary to change 1 gram of a substance from a liquid to a vapor without changing its temperature. The heat of vaporization of water is 540 cal/g.

EXAMPLES

1. How many calories are necessary to change 10 g of water at 100°C to steam at 100°C?

Since the heat of vaporization of water is 540 cal/g, the number of calories necessary will be:

$$540 \text{ cal/g} \times 10 \text{ g} = 5400 \text{ cal}.$$

2. How many calories are necessary to heat 10 g of ice at -10°C to steam at 120°C?

Calories to heat ice from - 10°C to 0°C.

> = mass × sp.ht of ice × temp. change
>
> = 10 g × 0.5 cal/g°C × 10°C
>
> = 50 cal.

Calories to melt ice

> = mass × ht. of fusion
>
> = 10 g × 80 cal/g
>
> = 800 cal.

Calories to heat water from 0°C to 100°C

> = mass × sp. of water × temp. change
>
> = 10 g × 1 cal/g°C × 100°C
>
> = 1000 cal.

Calories to change water at 100°C to steam at 100°C

> = mass × ht. of vaporization
>
> = 10 g × 540 cal/g
>
> = 5400 cal.

Calories to heat steam from 100°C to 120°C

> = mass × sp.ht of steam × temp. change
>
> = 10 g × 0.48 cal/g°C × 20°C
>
> = 96 cal.

Total heat required = 50 + 800 + 1000 + 5400 + 96 = 7346 cal.

3. Determine the resulting temperature when 100 g of ice at 0°C is mixed with 20 g of steam at 100°C.

Heat lost = heat gained

Calories required to melt ice

> = mass × ht of fusion
>
> = 100 g × 80 cal/g
>
> = 8000 cal.

Calories required to heat water from 0°C to final temperature

> = mass × sp.ht of water × temp. change
>
> = 100 g × 1 cal/g°C × (t-0)
>
> = 100 t cal.

Calories lost by steam at 100°C changing to water at 100°C.

> = mass × ht. of vaporization
>
> = 20 g × 540 cal/g
>
> = 10800 cal.

Calories lost by water at 100°C cooling to final temperature.

> = mass × sp. ht × temp. change
>
> = 20 g × 1 cal/g°C × (100−t)
>
> = 20 (100 − t) cal.

Heat lost = heat gained

$$10800 + 20 (100 - t) = 8000 + 100 t$$
$$10800 + 1000 - 20 t = 8000 + 100 t$$
$$120 t = 4800$$
$$t = 40°C$$

II. ENERGY RELATIONS IN CHEMICAL REACTIONS

A. Heat of Reaction

The number of calories that are evolved or absorbed in a chemical reaction is known as the heat of reaction. If heat is evolved in a chemical change, the reaction is said to be exothermic.

$$CH_4(g) + 2O_2(g) \longrightarrow CO_2(g) + 2H_2(\ell) + 212;930 \text{ cal.}$$

When 1 mole of gaseous methane reacts with 2 moles of gaseous oxygen to form 1 mole of gaseous carbon dioxide and 1 moles of liquid water, 212,930 calories of heat are evolved.

If heat is absorbed in a chemical change, the reaction is said to be endothermic.

$$C_{(graphite)} + 2S_{(S)} \longrightarrow CS_{2(\ell)} - 22,000 \text{ cal.}$$

When 1 gram-atom of carbon in the form of graphite reacts with 2 gram-atoms of solid sulfur to form 1 mole of liquid carbon disulfide, 22,000 calories of heat are absorbed.

If heat is evolved, the number of calories is indicated as a positive quantity on the right-hand side of the equation; if heat is absorbed, the number of calories is indicated as a negative quantity.

B. Heat of Formation

The heat of formation is the heat of reaction associated with the formation of one mole of a compound from its elements in their standard states. The standard state of an element is the form in which it commonly exists at room temperature and atmospheric pressure.

$$H_2{}_{(g)} + \frac{1}{2}O_2{}_{(g)} \longrightarrow H_2O_{(\ell)} + 68,400 \text{ cal.}$$

When 1 mole of liquid water is formed from 1 mole of gaseous hydrogen and 1/2 mole of gaseous oxygen, 68,400 calories of heat are evolved.

C. Additivity of Thermochemical Equations. The Law of Hess

The Law of Hess states that the heat evolved or absorbed in a chemical reaction is the same, whether it takes place in one or several steps. The overall heat change in a chemical reaction that takes place in several steps is the algebraic sum of the heats of reaction of the individual steps, and this total heat will be the same as the heat evolved or absorbed if the reaction took place in one step. Thus thermochemical equations may be added or subtracted, or they may be multiplied or divided by a constant factor. By this method heats of reaction, which are difficult to determine directly, may be calculated.

EXAMPLES

1. Determine the heat of formation of CO from the following equations.

    (1) $C_{(s)} + O_2{}_{(g)} \longrightarrow CO_2{}_{(g)} + 94,030 \text{ cal.}$

    (2) $CO_{(g)} + \frac{1}{2}O_2{}_{(g)} \longrightarrow CO_2{}_{(g)} + 67,600 \text{ cal.}$

Subtracting (2) from (1): $C_{(s)} + \frac{1}{2}O_2{}_{(g)} \longrightarrow \quad + 26,430 \text{ cal.}$

Rearranging: $C_{(s)} + \frac{1}{2}O_2{}_{(g)} \longrightarrow CO_{(g)} + 26,430 \text{ cal.}$

The heat of formation of CO is 26,430 cal.

2. Calculate the heat of formation of 1 mole of CH_4 from its elements from the following data.

    (1) $CH_4{}_{(g)} + 2O_2{}_{(g)} \longrightarrow CO_2{}_{(g)} + 2H_2O_{(\ell)} + 212,930 \text{ cal.}$

    (2) $C_{(s)} + O_2{}_{(g)} \longrightarrow CO_2{}_{(g)} + 94,030 \text{ cal.}$

    (3) $H_2{}_{(g)} + \frac{1}{2}O_2{}_{(g)} \longrightarrow H_2O_{(\ell)} + 68,400 \text{ cal.}$

Multiply (3) by 2, and add (2):

$$2H_{2(g)} + O_{2(g)} \longrightarrow 2H_2O_{(\ell)} + 136,800 \text{ cal.}$$

$$C_{(s)} + O_{2(g)} \longrightarrow CO_{2(g)} + 94,030 \text{ cal.}$$

(4) $\quad C_{(s)} + 2H_{2(g)} + 2O_{2(g)} \longrightarrow 2H_2O_{(\ell)} + CO_{2(g)} + 230,830 \text{ cal.}$

Subtract (1) from (4):

(4) $\quad C_{(s)} + 2H_{2(g)} + 2O_{2(g)} \longrightarrow 2H_2O_{(\ell)} + CO_{2(g)} + 230,830 \text{ cal.}$

(1) $\quad -CH_{4(g)} - 2O_{2(g)} \longrightarrow -CO_{2(g)} - 2H_2O_{(\ell)} - 212,930 \text{ cal.}$

$$C_{(s)} + 2H_{2(g)} - CH_{4(g)} \longrightarrow + 17,900 \text{ cal.}$$

Rearranging: $\quad C_{(s)} + 2H_{2(g)} \longrightarrow CH_4 + 17,900 \text{ cal.}$

The heat of formation of CH_4 is 17,900 cal.

PROBLEMS

(ANSWERS ON PAGE 158)

1. How many calories are necessary to heat each of the following from 20°C to 85°C? (a) 25 g of water (b) 20 g of glass (c) 40 g of iron (d) 25 g of zinc. The specific heats are: glass = 0.2; iron = 0.112; zinc = 0.093.

2. When 200 g of a metal at 20°C were placed in 500 g of boiling water, the system attained temperature equilibrium at 95°C. Calculate the specific heat of the metal.

3. When 220 g of a metal were heated to 100°C and placed in 400 g of water at 25°C, the system attained temperature equilibrium at 40°C. Calculate the specific heat of the metal.

4. How many calories are evolved when 200 g of steam at 150°C are cooled to ice at −50°C?

5. Determine the resulting temperature when 1000 g of ice at 0°C are mixed with 200 g of steam at 100°C.

6. Determine the final temperature when 2.4 lbs of steam at 212°F are passed into 66 lbs of water at 50°F.

7. From the data below calculate the heat of reaction of

$$Fe_2O_{3(s)} + 2Al_{(s)} \longrightarrow 2Fe_{(s)} + Al_2O_{3(s)}$$

$$2Fe_{(s)} + \frac{3}{2} O_{2(g)} \longrightarrow Fe_2O_{3(s)} + 198,500 \text{ cal.}$$

$$2Al_{(s)} + \frac{3}{2} O_{2(g)} \longrightarrow Al_2O_{3(s)} + 380,000 \text{ cal.}$$

8. From the data below calculate the heat of reaction of

$$C_{(s)} + CO_{2(g)} \longrightarrow 2CO_{(g)}$$

$$C_{(s)} + \frac{1}{2} O_{2(g)} \longrightarrow CO_{(g)} + 26,400 \text{ cal.}$$

$$CO_{(g)} + \frac{1}{2} O_{2(g)} \longrightarrow CO_{2(g)} + 67,000 \text{ cal.}$$

9. Calculate heat of formation of 1 mole of C_2H_6 from its elements from the following equations.

$$C_2H_{6(g)} + \frac{7}{2} O_{2(g)} \longrightarrow 2CO_{2(g)} + 3H_2O_{(\ell)} + 372,800 \text{ cal.}$$

$$C_{(s)} + O_{2(g)} \longrightarrow CO_{2(g)} + 94,030 \text{ cal.}$$

$$H_{2(g)} + \frac{1}{2} O_{2(g)} \longrightarrow H_2O_{(\ell)} + 68,400 \text{ cal.}$$

10. Calculate the heat of formation of ethyl alcohol C_2H_5OH from its elements.

$$C_2H_5OH_{(\ell)} + 3O_{2(g)} \longrightarrow 2CO_{2(g)} + 3H_2O_{(\ell)} + 327,000 \text{ cal.}$$

$$C_{(s)} + O_{2(g)} \longrightarrow CO_{2(g)} + 94,030 \text{ cal.}$$

$$H_{2(g)} + \frac{1}{2} O_{2(g)} \longrightarrow H_2O_{(\ell)} + 68,400 \text{ cal.}$$

RADIOACTIVITY AND TRANSMUTATION OF ELEMENTS

I. RADIOACTIVITY AND NATURE OF RADIATION

Certain substances affect photographic plates even when they are separated from them by sheets of black paper. Thus these substances emit some types of powerful radiation or rays. One or more of the following three types of rays are emitted.

A. ALPHA PARTICLES (α)

An unstable nucleus may become relatively more stable by ejecting an alpha particle. This is a high speed helium nucleus carrying a double positive charge and represented He^{2+}. It has mass 4 amu and may be regarded as a particle of 2 protons united with 2 neutrons. The new element formed will have a mass number 4 units less and an atomic number 2 units less than the element which emitted the alpha particle.

$$_{92}U^{238} \longrightarrow {}_2He^4 + {}_{90}Th^{234}$$
$$\text{alpha particle}$$

Subscripts are atomic numbers and superscripts are mass numbers.

B. BETA PARTICLES (β)

Beta particles are high speed electrons. Loss of an electron by a nucleus has no effect on the mass number of the atom. However, loss of -1 unit of charge leaves the nucleus with 1 extra positive charge. There is a new element produced, with atomic number 1 greater than the previous element.

$$_{90}Th^{234} \longrightarrow {}_{-1}e^0 + {}_{91}Pa^{234}$$
$$\text{beta particle}$$

C. GAMMA RAYS

Like light, gamma rays are a type of electromagnetic radiation. They are similar to X-rays and have equal energies.

Emission of gamma rays leaves a nucleus of the same element with less energy.

II. RADIOACTIVE DISINTEGRATION LAW

In general, the rate at which particular radioactive atoms break down to others is not influenced by chemical changes or temperature. The half life of a radioactive species is a measure of the time in which half of any mass of that element will have changed to a relatively more stable atom. For example, U-238 atoms have a half-life of 4.65 $\times 10^9$ years. If a sample of this isotope now weighs 1 g, in 4.65×10^9 years half the number of U-238 atoms will have decayed by alpha particle emission to a relatively more stable type of atom. Similarly, Carbon-14 which is radioactive has a half-life of 5,600 years. This indicates that in any 5,600 year period the number of carbon-14 atoms remaining will be one half of the number present 5,600 years before.

III. ARTIFICIAL TRANSMUTATION OF ELEMENTS

Artificial transmutation of non-radioactive elements has been accomplished by nuclear bombardment with high energy particles. In a balanced nuclear equation the sum of the masses of the colliding particles must equal the sum of the masses of the products (the superscripts), and the sum of the charges (the subscripts) must also be equal.

Note also that atoms of the same nuclear charge are isotopes of the same element and thus have the same symbol, as in $_{92}U^{238}$ and $_{92}U^{235}$.

If the nuclear charge differs, the atoms are of different elements, as in $_{11}Na^{24}$ and $_{12}Mg^{24}$.

A. ALPHA PARTICLE BOMBARDMENT

1. Emission of a Proton

$$_{13}Al^{27} + {}_{2}He^4 \longrightarrow {}_{14}Si^{30} + {}_{1}H^1 \text{ (a proton)}$$

$$(27 + 4) = (30 + 1) \text{ and } (13 + 2) = (14 + 1)$$

2. Emission of a Neutron

$$_{5}B^{11} + {}_{2}He^4 \longrightarrow {}_{7}N^{14} + {}_{0}n^1 \text{ (a neutron)}$$

$$(11 + 4) = (14 + 1) \text{ and } (5 + 2) = (7 + 0)$$

B. PROTON BOMBARDMENT

$$_{3}Li^7 + {}_{1}H^1 \longrightarrow {}_{2}He^4 + {}_{2}He^4$$

C. DEUTERON BOMBARDMENT

$$_{3}Li^7 + {}_{1}H^2 \longrightarrow {}_{4}Be^8 + {}_{0}n^1$$

IV. INDUCED RADIOACTIVITY AND NATURAL RADIOACTIVITY

Natural radioactive atoms occur on earth and were not made by man. U-235 and U-238 are examples. Other unstable atoms not found on earth are made by nuclear bombardment of non-radioactive stable atoms. Thus radioactivity may be induced.

Nucleons.

The term nucleon is applied to both the neutrons and protons of a nucleus. The stability of a particular radioactive atom and therefore its half life depends on the proportion of the two types of nucleon, protons and neutrons. Some atoms may be regarded as being so unstable that the nucleus exists for a very brief time.

For example, the first radioactive product in the following cases decays to a more stable form.

A. ALPHA PARTICLE BOMBARDMENT

$$_5B^{10} + {}_2He^4 \longrightarrow {}_7N^{13} + {}_0n^1$$

then $_7N^{13} \longrightarrow {}_6C^{13} + {}_{+1}e^0$ (a positron)

The positron is the same as an electron except that its charge is positive. Loss of a positron causes a decrease of 1 in the atomic number.

B. PROTON BOMBARDMENT

$$_6C^{12} + {}_1H^1 \longrightarrow {}_7N^{13} \text{ (this decays as in the previous equation)}$$

C. NEUTRON BOMBARDMENT

$$_{11}Na^{23} + {}_0n^1 \longrightarrow {}_{11}Na^{24}$$

then $_{11}Na^{24} \longrightarrow {}_{12}Mg^{24} + {}_{-1}e^0$

Note that balance still applies as in the atomic charge numbers

$$11 = (12 - 1)$$

D. ELECTRON BOMBARDMENT

$$_4Be^9 + {}_{-1}e^0 \longrightarrow {}_3Li^8 + {}_0n^1$$

then $_3Li^8 \longrightarrow {}_4Be^8 + {}_{-1}e^0$

142

E. DEUTERON BOMBARDMENT

$$_{11}Na^{23} + {}_{1}H^{2} \longrightarrow {}_{11}Na^{24} + {}_{1}H^{1}$$

then the Na-24 breaks down as in case C.

V. ATOMIC FISSION

Atomic or nuclear fission is caused by neutrons which break up atoms such as U^{235} or Pu^{239} into atoms of smaller atomic weight with the release of large amounts of energy. In a nuclear fission a portion of matter is converted into energy.

$$_{92}U^{235} + {}_{0}n^{1} \longrightarrow {}_{56}Ba^{139} + {}_{36}Kr^{88} + neutrons$$

The neutrons may be emitted as energy, or if the sample of U^{235} is large enough, the neutrons may be captured by other atoms of U^{235}, thus setting up a chain reaction or self-perpetuating process. In order to prevent premature explosions, only less than critical quantities of U^{235} may be kept in one place. In the atomic bomb, two specimens of less than critical size are caused to come together at the desired instant of explosion.

PROBLEMS

(ANSWERS ON PAGE 158)

1. What 3 types of particles are emitted by radioactive substances?

2. Give the mass numbers and the charges of the 3 particles.

3. How does the position of an element in the periodic table change by the emission of (a) an alpha particle? (b) a beta particle?

4. (a) State the radioactive disintegration law.
   (b) What is half-life?

5. What particles are used for nuclear bombardment in artificial transmutation?

6. What is induced radioactivity?

7. Complete the following equations.

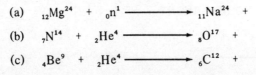

(a) $\quad _{12}Mg^{24} + {}_{0}n^{1} \longrightarrow {}_{11}Na^{24} +$

(b) $\quad _{7}N^{14} + {}_{2}He^{4} \longrightarrow {}_{8}O^{17} +$

(c) $\quad _{4}Be^{9} + {}_{2}He^{4} \longrightarrow {}_{6}C^{12} +$

(d) $_{13}Al^{27}$ + $_2He^4$ ⟶ $_{15}P^{30}$ +

(e) $_7N^{14}$ + $_0n^1$ ⟶ $_5B^{11}$ +

(f) $_{15}P^{31}$ + $_0n^1$ ⟶ $_{13}Al^{28}$ +

(g) $_{11}Na^{24}$ ⟶ $_{12}Mg^{24}$ +

EXPONENTS

I. DEFINITION

The symbol b^m is read "the mth power of b" or "b to the mth".
The quantity b is called the base and the quantity m is called the
exponent.

II. POSITIVE EXPONENTS

If m is a positive integer, b^m denotes the product of m factors each
equal to b, or

$$b^m = b \cdot b \cdot b \text{-----} b, \text{ m factors b}$$

EXAMPLES

1. $10^2 = 10 \times 10 = 100$

2. $10^3 = 10 \times 10 \times 10 = 1000$

3. $10^5 = 10 \times 10 \times 10 \times 10 \times 10 = 100,000$

   If m is zero, $b^0 = 1$

EXAMPLES

1. $10^0 = 1$

2. $-3 \times 10^0 = -3 \times 1 = -3$

3. $(-3 \times 10^2)^0 = 1$

III. NEGATIVE EXPONENTS

If m is a negative quantity, $b^{-m} = \left(\dfrac{1}{b}\right)^m = \dfrac{1}{b^m}$

144

EXAMPLES

1. $10^{-1} = \dfrac{1}{10}$

2. $10^{-4} = \dfrac{1}{10^4} = \dfrac{1}{10,000}$

3. $\left(\dfrac{2}{3}\right)^{-2} = \left(\dfrac{3}{2}\right)^{2} = \dfrac{9}{4}$

4. $\dfrac{6}{2 \times 10^{-3}} = \dfrac{3}{10^{-3}} = \dfrac{3}{\left(\frac{1}{10}\right)^3} = 3 \times 10^3 = 3000$

IV. FRACTIONAL EXPONENTS

If m is a fraction that is if $m = \dfrac{p}{q}$, where p and q are integers, then

$b^{p/q} = \left(\sqrt[q]{b}\;^{p}\right)$ or $b^{p/q}$ means: take the qth root of m and raise it to the pth power.

EXAMPLES

1. $10^{\frac{1}{2}} = \sqrt{10}$

2. $8^{\frac{2}{3}} = \left(\sqrt[3]{8}\right)^2 = 2^2 = 4$

3. $\left(\dfrac{1}{27}\right)^{\frac{1}{3}} = \sqrt[3]{\dfrac{1}{27}} = \dfrac{1}{3}$

V. MULTIPLICATION

To multiply numbers that have the same base, add the exponents:

$$b^m \cdot b^n = b^{m+n}$$

EXAMPLES

1. $b^7 \cdot b^{11} = b^{7+11} = b^{18}$

2. $10^{-5} \cdot 10^3 = 10^{-5+3} = 10^{-2} = \dfrac{1}{10^2} = \dfrac{1}{100}$

3. $(3 \times 4^5)(7 \times 4^{-4}) = 21 \times 4 = 84$

VI. DIVISION

To divide numbers that have the same base, subtract the exponents:

$$\dfrac{b^m}{b^n} = b^{m-n}$$

EXAMPLES

1. $\dfrac{b^{10}}{b^3} = b^{10-3} = b^7$

2. $\dfrac{2.8 \times 10^{-5}}{0.4 \times 10^2} = 7 \times 10^{-5-2} = 7 \times 10^{-7}$

3. $\dfrac{5 \times 10^2}{2 \times 10^{-1}} = 2.5 \times 10^{2-(-1)} = 2.5 \times 10^{2+1} = 2.5 \times 10^3$

VII. RAISING TO POWERS

In raising to powers, exponents are multiplied:

$$(b^m)^n = b^{m \cdot n}$$

EXAMPLES

1. $(10^2)^3 = 10^{2 \times 3} = 10^6$

2. $(10^{1/2})^4 = 10^{1/2 \times 4} = 10^2$

3. $(4^{-3})^3 = 4^{-3 \times 3} = 4^{-9}$

VIII. LARGE AND SMALL NUMBERS

The true significance of very large numbers or of very small numbers may be obscure because of the many digits or zeros that are required to express them. A clearer and also a more convenient presentation is effected by expressing very large and very small numbers as the product of two numbers, one of which is an integral power of 10.

4. $5000 = 5 \times 10^3$

5. $0.0036 = 3.6 \times 10^{-3}$

6. $0.00000000046 = 4.6 \times 10^{-10}$

7. $602,280,000,000,000,000,000,000, = 6.0228 \times 10^{23}$

PROBLEMS

(ANSWERS ON PAGE 159)

Evaluate the following and express the results in powers of 10.

1. 1300×200

2. $0.630 \div 90$

3. $(8,000,000)^{2/3}$

146

4. $700 \div (2 \times 10)^0$

5. $\dfrac{0.0035}{500 \times 7}$

6. $\dfrac{(0.00004)^4 \times (6,000)}{(0.0002)^3 \times (80)^2}$

7. $\sqrt{24 \times 10^{-7}} \times \sqrt{6 \times 10^5}$

8. $64(4 \times 10^2)^{-3}$

9. $\dfrac{413 \times 4.13}{0.000413}$

10. $\dfrac{(2 \times 10^2)^3 \times (3 \times 10^{-5})^2}{(0.000072)}$

11. $(2 \times 3.4)^2 \div 0.0017$

12. $\sqrt[3]{8,000,000} \times \sqrt[3]{0.027}$

APPROXIMATE NUMBERS AND SIGNIFICANT FIGURES

I. ROUND-OFF

In any discussion of approximate numbers, it is necessary to understand the meaning of "round-off". To round-off 61.8 to two digits means to express it as the closest two-digit number. Since 61.8 is between 61 and 62, but closer to 62, then the result of the round-off is 62. Similarly, if 61.3 is rounded off to two digits, the result is 61.

What about 61.5? It is equally close to 61 and 62. In this case and similar ones, round off to the nearest even number of 62· Note that 62.5 rounded off to two digits is also 62, the nearest even number. The following numbers are rounded off to three digits.

$$21.2378 \longrightarrow 21.2$$
$$6.0812 \longrightarrow 6.08$$
$$316.50 \longrightarrow 316$$
$$9.835 \longrightarrow 9.84$$

II. APPROXIMATE NUMBERS

In any experimental situation, the numbers obtained are approximate. That is, they are accurate only to the degree allowed by the measuring instruments. For example, if a thermometer is marked off in intervals of one degree and if the column of mercury stands between 72° and 73°, then the temperature can be read accurately only to the nearest degree — either 72° or 73°, whichever is closer. It may actually be 72.3°, but the measuring instrument allows us only the approximate value 72°.

III. SIGNIFICANT FIGURES

The significant figures of any number are its digits except for those zeros that serve only to locate the decimal point. Other zeros are significant. For example, 0.032 and 0.0032 each contains only two significant figures. The zeros involved serve only to locate the decimal point. The number 320, on the other hand, may contain two or three significant figures depending on the context. That is, there may be exactly 320 beans in a jar, or exactly 320 pages in a book. The 320 contains three significant figures. Conversely, 320 may represent the approximate number of feet between two trees. Then 320 contains only two significant figures 3 and 2 — the zero serving only to p'ace the decimal point.

61.053 contains five significant figures and 75.10 contains four significant figures (the zero on the end indicates that the number has been rounded off from 75.103 or 75.102, etc.). If 93,000 is an approximate rather than an exact number, it is customary to write it as 9.3×10^4. The approximate number 0.0005 may be written as 5×10^{-4}. The significant figures are then apparent.

IV. ADDITION AND SUBTRACTION

When adding (or subtracting) approximate numbers, round off the sum (or difference) so that the result has significant figures only below columns in which each approximate number has a significant figure.

EXAMPLES

1. Add:

$$
\begin{array}{r}
61.02 \\
3.14032 \\
2.1530 \\
\hline
66.31332
\end{array}
$$

The sum is 66.31

2. Subtract:

$$
\begin{array}{r}
16.257 \\
-\ 3.615 \\
\hline
12.642
\end{array}
$$

The difference is 12.642

V. MULTIPLICATION AND DIVISION

When multiplying (or dividing) approximate numbers, round off the product (or quotient) so that the result contains only as many significant figures as the least accurate approximate number involved.

EXAMPLES

1. $2.01 \times 1.2 = 2.412$

   The product is 2.4.

2. If 3.1416 is divided by 60.1, the result should be rounded off to three significant figures.

PROBLEMS

(ANSWERS ON PAGE 158)

1. State the number of significant figures contained in each of the following:

   (a) 3.14159   (f) 6.3×10^5

   (b) 6.021   (g) 9.108×10^{-4}

   (c) 0.00357   (h) 454

   (d) 0.106   (i) 0.2056

   (e) 51.20   (j) 1.0060

2. Add:

   (a) 601.   (b) 12.315   (c) 0.096
          7.   4.0   0.351
          0.25   7.48   0.6105

3. Subtract:

   (a) 21.3   (b) 385.08   (c) 65.
          6.2   16.1   0.2

4. Multiply:

   (a) 3.21×0.2

   (b) 61.2×0.031

   (c) 122×0.120

5. Divide:

   (a) $96.43 \div 3.45$

   (b) $12.31 \div 0.612$

   (c) $0.016 \div 0.004$

149

ANSWER KEY TO PROBLEMS

ANSWERS TO PROBLEMS, PAGE 10

1. (a) 25.4 cm   (b) 254 mm   (c) 0.254 m
2. (a) 19.69 in   (b) 0.547 yd   (c) 1.64 ft
3. 2 liters
4. 1406 g per cm^2
5. (a) 50,000 mg   (b) 0.05 kg   (c) 0.11 lb
6. (a) 3.78 liters   (b) .3780 ml
7. (a) 6.0×10^{-7} cm   (b) 2.36×10^{-7} in
8. (a) 20°C   (b) -16.7°C   (c) 83.3°F
9. (a) 68°F   (b) 122°F   (c) 104°F
10. (a) -38.3°C   (b) -49°F   (c) -58.3°C
11. (a) 385°A   (b) 233°K   (c) 351°A
12. (a) 1017°C   (b) 28°C   (c) -110°C
13. 0.09 lb/in^3
14. 249.6 lb/ft^3
15. 0.0268 km/sec
16. (a) 10^5 millimicrons   (b) 10^{-2} cm   (c) 0.00394 in
17. (a) 2.54×10^5 microns   (b) 2.54×10^8 millimicrons   (c) 2.54×10^9 in

ANSWERS TO PROBLEMS, PAGE 13

1. (a) 5 g/ml   (b) 5
2. (a) 2.5 g/ml   (b) 2.5
3. 2.5
4. 2.6
5. (a) 0.667   (b) 0.667 g/ml
6. (a) 65.8 ml   (b) 25.9 ml
7. 27,770 lb
8. (a) 21.3   (b) 4260 g
9. (a) 930 g   (b) 1.86 g/ml   (c) 269 ml
10. (a) 884 g   (b) 28.3 ml
11. (a) 750 ml   (b) 0.024 c ft
12. 1.28 g/liter

ANSWERS TO PROBLEMS, PAGE 19

1. 38.95 liters
2. 317 ml
3. 455 ml
4. 208 ml
5. 17.9 l.
6. 1450 ml
7. 457 mm

8. 1.57 atm
9. 438 ml
10. 888 ml
11. 1.26 g/l
12. 0.093 g/l
13. 26.85 g
14. 1.22 g

ANSWERS TO PROBLEMS, PAGE 23

1. (a) NaBr   (b) KCl   (c) MgS   (d) CaF_2 (e) AlI_3
2. (a) silver iodide   (b) sodium oxide   (c) zinc bromide   (d) barium sulfide   (e) aluminum oxide.

ANSWERS TO PROBLEMS, PAGE 24

1. (a) $CuCl_2$ (b) SnF_2 (c) $SbBr_3$ (d) Fe_2S_3 (e) HgO
2. (a) iron (II) oxide or ferrous oxide   (b) phosphorus (III) chloride or phosphorous chloride   (c) mercury (I) iodide or mercurous iodide   (d) antimony (V) oxide or antimonic oxide   (e) copper (I) chloride or cuprous chloride.

ANSWERS TO PROBLEMS, PAGE 29

1. (a) $KClO_3$ (b) Ag_2CO_3 (c) $CaSO_4$ (d) Hg_3PO_4 (e) $Fe_2(SO_4)_3$ (f) $Al(ClO_4)_3$ (g) $Ba(HCOO)_2$
2. (a) sodium carbonate   (b) copper (II) sulfate   (c) potassium perbromate   (d) zinc chlorite   (e) aluminum phosphite   (f) arsenic (V) phosphate

ANSWERS TO PROBLEMS, PAGE 31

1. (a) NaI   (b) K_2O (c) $CaBr_2$ (d) CCl_4 (e) Ag_2S
2. (a) silver chloride   (b) magnesium iodide   (c) tin (II) or stannous bromide   (d) iron (II) or ferric chloride   (e) mercury (I) or mercurous bromide   (f) copper (I) or cuprous oxide
3. (a) PBr_3 (b) $FeCl_2$ (c) As_2O_5 (d) CuS   (e) CuO   (f) HgO   (g) BiI_3 (h) SnO_2

4. (a) + 1 (b) + 1 (c) + 2 (d) + 3 (e) + 2 (g) + 5 (h) + 4

5. (a) NaOH (b) $Ca(OH)_2$ (c) $Al(OH)_3$ (d) $Sn(OH)_2$ (e) $Sn(OH)_4$
   (f) $Fe(OH)_2$

6. (a) O_2 (b) O_3 (c) N_2 (d) P_4 (e) H_2O_2 (f) BaO_2 (g) HCl

7. (a) potassium hydroxide (b) zinc hydroxide (c) aluminum
   hydroxide (d) tin (IV) hydroxide (e) iron (III) hydroxide
   (f) barium hydroxide

8. (a) hydrogen iodide, hydriodic acid (b) hydrogen phosphite,
   phosphorous acid (c) hydrogen nitrate, nitric acid
   (d) hydrogen sulfite, sulfurous acid (e) hydrogen chlorate,
   chloric acid (f) hydrogen perchlorate, perchloric acid

9. (a) HBr (b) H_3PO_4 (c) HNO_3 (d) H_2SO_4 (e) HClO (f) $HClO_2$

10. (a) ammonium sulfite (b) iron (II) sulfite (c) copper (I) sulfate
    (d) tin (II) nitrate (e) iron (II) phosphate (f) iron (II) chlorite

11. (a) $Fe_2(SO_4)_3$ (b) $CuSO_3$ (c) NH_4NO_2 (d) $Sn_3(PO_4)_4$ (e) $FePO_4$
    (f) Cu_2O (g) FeF_2 (h) SnO_2

12. (a) $Cr_2(SO_4)_3$ (b) CrI_2 (c) NH_4NO_3 (d) $HgSO_4$
    (e) Hg_2O (f) $ZnCO_3$ (g) $CaSiO_3$ (h) $Mg(NO_3)_2$
    (i) Al_2S_3 (j) Cu_2O (k) $CuSO_4$ (l) $BaCO_3$
    (m) K_2SiO_3 (n) $KClO_4$ (o) $Fe(ClO_3)_2$ (p) Ag_3PO_4
    (q) $AgClO_3$ (r) NaClO (s) KNO_3 (t) $NaNO_2$

13. (a) ammonium sulfate   (b) ammonium phosphate
    (c) copper (II) sulfate   (d) silver oxide
    (e) silver phosphate   (f) tin (II) oxide
    (g) mercury (I) oxide   (h) zinc sulfate
    (i) sodium sulfite   (j) ammonium hydroxide
    (k) carbon dioxide   (l) carbon monoxide
    (m) zinc sulfide   (n) aluminum hydroxide
    (o) sodium chlorite   (p) potassium hypochlorite
    (q) sodium hydrogen carbonate (r) sodium perchlorate
    (s) zinc silicate   (t) mercury (II) iodide

14. (a) H^+ (b) H_3O^+ (c) Na^+ (d) Mg^{2+} (e) S^{2-} (f) Fe^{2+} (g) Cl^-
    (h) Cu^+ (i) O^{2-} (j) Mn^{2+} (k) ClO_3^- (l) HSO_3^- (m) NH_4^+
    (n) HCO_3^- (o) F^- (p) PO_4^{3-}

ANSWERS TO PROBLEMS, PAGE 38

1. (a) 1 mole (b) 2.5 moles (c) 8.9 moles (d) 0.026 moles

2. (a) 96.2 g S, (b) 9.8 g Zn (c) 282.9 g Co, (d) 0.27 g Al

152

3. $0.2 \times 6.02 \times 10^{23}$ (or 1.2×10^{23}) Sn atoms

4. 3.15×10^{-23} g

5. 2.32×10^{-23} g

6. 54.9 amu, manganese

7. (a) 146 amu   (b) 98 amu   (c) 58 amu

8. (a) 74 amu   (b) 342 amu   (c) 246 amu   (d) 262 amu

9. (a) 12.5 moles   (b) 5.6 moles   (c) 2 moles   (d) 0.05 moles

10. (a) 78.75 g   (b) 560 g   (c) 1.12 g   (d) 2505 g

11. $0.3 \times 6.02 \times 10^{23}$ (or 1.8×10^{23}) molecules

12. $2 \times 8 \times 6.02 \times 10^{23}$ (or 9.63×10^{22}) atoms of sodium

ANSWERS TO PROBLEMS, PAGE 43

1. (a) Na 0.153, I 0.847   (b) Na 15.3% I 84.7%

2. (a) K 0.552   P 0.146   O 0.302   (b) K 55.2% P 14.6% O 30.2%

3. (a) Na 74.3% O 25.7%   (b) K 69.6% O 28.6% H 1.8%
   (c) Ag 56.4% Cl 18.5% O 25.1%   (d) Pb 62.6% N 8.5% O 28.9%
   (e) C 49.0% H 2.7% Cl 48.3%

4. %H_2O is 62.9

5. SF_6

6. $C_3H_8O_3$

7. PCl_5

8. (a) NH_2 (b) N_2H_4

9. S_2Cl_2

10. $C_2H_4O_2$

11. 42, CH_3

12. $KF.2H_2O$

ANSWERS TO PROBLEMS, PAGE 45

(a) $2KClO_3 \longrightarrow 2KCl + 3O_2$

(b) $2HgO \longrightarrow 2Hg + O_2$

(c) $P_4 + 10Cl_2 \longrightarrow 4PCl_5$

(d) $2FeCl_2 + Cl_2 \longrightarrow 2FeCl_3$

(e) $Ca(OH)_2 + 2HNO_3 \longrightarrow Ca(NO_3)_2 + 2H_2O$

(f) $3Zn + 2H_3PO_4 \longrightarrow Zn_3(PO_4)_2 + 3H_2$

ANSWERS TO PROBLEMS, PAGE 53

1. (a) $2Na + Br_2 \longrightarrow 2NaBr$
   (b) $2K + I_2 \longrightarrow 2KI$
   (c) $2Ca + O_2 \longrightarrow 2CaO$
   (d) $Ba + Cl_2 \longrightarrow BaCl_2$
   (e) $H_2 + Br_2 \longrightarrow 2HBr$
   (f) $2Al + 3Br_2 \longrightarrow 2AlBr_3$
   (g) $Zn + Cl_2 \longrightarrow ZnCl_2$
   (h) $CaO + SO_2 \longrightarrow CaSO_3$
   (i) $K_2O + SO_3 \longrightarrow K_2SO_4$
   (j) $Cu + Cl_2 \longrightarrow CuCl_2$

2. (a) $2NaClO_3 \longrightarrow 2NaCl + 3O_2$
   (b) $2KNO_3 \longrightarrow 2KNO_2 + O_2$
   (c) $MgCO_3 \longrightarrow MgO + CO_2$
   (d) $2NaNO_3 \longrightarrow 2NaNO_2 + O_2$
   (e) $2BaO_2 \longrightarrow 2BaO + O_2$
   (f) $2Ag_2O \longrightarrow 4Ag + O_2$

3. (a) $Cd + 2HCl \longrightarrow CdCl_2 + H_2$
   (b) $2Cr + 3H_2SO_4 \longrightarrow Cr_2(SO_4)_3 + 3H_2$
   (c) N.R.
   (d) $3Zn + 2H_3PO_4 \longrightarrow Zn_3(PO_4)_2 + 3H_2$
   (e) $2Zn + Pt(SO_4)_2 \longrightarrow 2ZnSO_4 + Pt$
   (f) $Cr + HgCl_2 \longrightarrow CrCl_2 + Hg$
   (g) N.R.
   (h) $Fe + SnSO_4 \longrightarrow FeSO_4 + Sn$

4. (a) $2AgNO_3 + Na_2CrO_4 \longrightarrow Ag_2CrO_4 + 2NaNO_3$
   (b) $BaCl_2 + Na_2CO_3 \longrightarrow BaCO_3 + 2NaCl$
   (c) $CuSO_4 + H_2S \longrightarrow CuS + H_2SO_4$
   (d) $ZnCl_2 + H_2S \longrightarrow ZnS + 2HCl$
   (e) $3AgNO_3 + H_3PO_4 \longrightarrow Ag_3PO_4 + 3HNO_3$
   (f) $Pb(NO_3)_2 + 2HCl \longrightarrow PbCl_2 + 2HNO_3$
   (g) $2AsCl_3 + 3H_2S \longrightarrow As_2Cl_3 + 3HCl$
   (h) $MnCl_2 + H_2S \longrightarrow MnS + 2HCl$

5. (a) $2K + 2H_2O \longrightarrow 2KOH + H_2$
   (b) $Sr + 2H_2O \longrightarrow Sr(OH)_2 + H_2$
   (c) $Zn + H_2O \longrightarrow ZnO + H_2$
   (d) $Cd + H_2O \longrightarrow CdO + H_2$
   (e) $2Al + 6HCl \longrightarrow 2AlCl_3 + 3H_2$
   (f) N.R.
   (g) $Mg + H_2SO_4 \longrightarrow MgSO_4 + H_2$
   (h) $Zn + FeSO_4 \longrightarrow ZnSO_4 + Fe$
   (i) $Fe + 2AgNO_3 \longrightarrow Fe(NO_3)_2 + 2Ag$
   (j) $2Au_2O_3 \longrightarrow 4Au + 3O_2$
   (k) N.R.
   (l) $2Ag_2O \longrightarrow 4Ag + O_2$

6. (a) $2Fe(OH)_3 \longrightarrow Fe_2O_3 + 3H_2O$
   (b) $Zn(OH)_2 \longrightarrow ZnO + H_2O$
   (c) N.R.
   (d) N.R.
   (e) $CaCO_3 \longrightarrow CaO + CO_2$
   (f) $2HgNO_3 \longrightarrow 2Hg + 2NO_2 + O_2$
   (g) $4Fe(NO_3)_2 \longrightarrow 2Fe_2O_3 + 8NO_2 + O_2$
   (h) N.R.
   (i) N.R.
   (j) $2HgCO_3 \longrightarrow 2Hg + 2CO_2 + O_2$

154

ANSWERS TO PROBLEMS, PAGE 56

1. 50 g
2. 32 g
3. 14.6 g
4. 36 g
5. (a) 23.3 g   (b) 291.7 g

6. 241 g
7. 138 g
8. (a) 1.17 g   (b) 3.4 g
9. 111.5 ml
10. 1480 ml

ANSWERS TO PROBLEMS, PAGE 61

1. 30.8
2. 107
3. 80
4. 54
5. (a) 0.71 g   (b) 1.52 g
   (c) 3.17 g   (d) 1.34 g
   (e) 1.43 g
6. (a) 1.25 g   (b) 0.18
   (c) 1.78   (d) 4.64   (e) 1.96
7. 4.44 l.
8. 9.87 l.

9. 3.59 l.
10. 49.4
11. 0.36 g
12. 10.4 g
13. 77.7 l.
14. 295 l.
15. 1.71 g
16. 72.3%
17. C_6H_6
18. C_2H_6

ANSWERS TO PROBLEMS, PAGE 65

1. 20 ml
2. 60 ml NO,   30 ml O_2
3. (a) 3.5 liters   (b) 1.75 liters
4. 3 liters CO_2 and 4.5 liters
   of steam
5. 10 ml C_3H_8,   50 ml O_2
6. 15 liters N_2 and 45 liters H_2

7. 90 ml
8. 120 ml CO_2,   100 ml O_2
9. 200 ml NH_3,   250 ml O_2
10. 375 liters
11. 250 liters
12. 20 ml O_2,   100 ml N_2

ANSWERS TO PROBLEMS, PAGE 69

1. 40
2. 23
3. 96

4. (a) 112 (b) 42
5. 10
6. 7

7. 9
8. 30
9. 18.6
10. 120

ANSWERS TO PROBLEMS, PAGE 72

1. (a) O   (b) O   (c) O   (d) -1   (e) +1   (f) O   (g) O   (h) O
2. (a) -2   (b) +4   (c) +5   (d) +5   (e) +6

ANSWERS TO PROBLEMS, PAGE 80

1. $3H_2S + 2HNO_3 \longrightarrow 3S + 2NO + 4H_2O$
2. $H_2S + 8HNO_3 \longrightarrow H_2SO_4 + 8NO_2 + 4H_2O$
3. $8HI + H_2SO_4 \longrightarrow 4I_2 + H_2S + 4H_2O$
4. $2HBr + H_2SO_4 \longrightarrow Br_2 + SO_2 + 2H_2O$
5. $2KMnO_4 + 16HBr \longrightarrow 5Br_2 + 2MnBr_2 + 2KBr + 8H_2O$
6. $2KMnO_4 + 2H_2S + 2H_2SO_4 \longrightarrow S + 2MnSO_4 + K_2SO_4 + 4H_2O$
7. $2K_2Cr_2O_7 + 3H_2S + 4H_2SO_4 \longrightarrow 3S + 2Cr_2(SO_4)_3 + 2K_2SO_4 + 7H_2O$
8. $S + 2H_2SO_4 \longrightarrow 3SO_2 + 2H_2O$
9. $6NaOH + 3Br_2 \longrightarrow NaBrO_3 + 5NaBr + 3H_2O$
10. $S + 6HNO_3 \longrightarrow H_2SO_4 + 6NO_2 + 2H_2O$

1. $3S^{-2} + 2NO_2^- + 8H^+ \longrightarrow 3S^0 + 2NO + 4H_2O$
2. $Pb^0 + 4H^+ + 2NO_3^- \longrightarrow Pb^{+2} + 2NO_2 + 2H_2O$
3. $3Cd^0 + 8H^+ + 2NO_3^- \longrightarrow 3Cd^{+2} + 2NO + 4H_2O$
4. $2MnO_4^- + 16H^+ + 10Cl^- \longrightarrow 2Mn^{+2} + 5Cl_2 + 8H_2O$
5. $2MnO_4^- + 16H^+ + 5S^{2-} \longrightarrow 2Mn^{+2} + 5S + 8H_2O$
6. $2Cr_2O_7^{2-} + 28H^+ + 6S^{2-} \longrightarrow 6S + 4Cr^{+3} + 14H_2O$

ANSWERS TO PROBLEMS, PAGE 83

1. $2CO + O_2 \longrightarrow 2CO_2$
2. $Cu + 4HNO_3 \longrightarrow Cu(NO_3)_2 + 2NO_2 + 2H_2O$
3. $3Fe + 8HNO_3 \longrightarrow 3Fe(NO_3)_2 + 2NO + 4H_2O$
4. $2FeSO_4 + 2HNO_3 + H_2SO_4 \longrightarrow Fe_2(SO_4)_3 + 2H_2O + 2NO$
5. $H_2SO_4 + 2HNO_3 \longrightarrow H_2SO_4 + 2NO_2 + H_2O$
6. $16HBr + 2KMnO_4 \longrightarrow 2KBr + 2MnBr_2 + 8H_2O + 5Br_2$
7. $14HBr + K_2Cr_2O_7 \longrightarrow 2CrBr_3 + 2KBr + 3Br_2 + 7H_2O$
8. $2NaCl + MnO_2 + 2H_2SO_4 \longrightarrow Na_2SO_4 + MnSO_4 + 2H_2O + Cl_2$
9. $5H_2S + 2KMnO_4 + 3H_2SO_4 \longrightarrow 2MnSO_4 + 5S + K_2SO_4 + 8H_2O$
10. $3H_2S + K_2Cr_2O_7 + 4H_2SO_4 \longrightarrow 3S + K_2SO_4 + Cr_2(SO_4)_3 + 7H_2O$

ANSWERS TO PROBLEMS, PAGE 88

1. (a) 27.8   (b) 45.8   (c) 78   (d) 102
2. (a) 3   (b) 206.7
3. (a) 2   (b) 24.3
4. (a) 9   (b) 3
5. 55.8
6. 51.9
7. 24.2
8. 55.8

156

9. 96
10. (a) lp, le, ln (b) 8p, 8e, 8n (c) 13p, 13e, 14n
    (d) 93p, 93e, 145n
11. 63.6

ANSWERS TO PROBLEMS, PAGE 96

1. (a) 53 (b) 143 (c) 71 (d) 32.7 (e) 37 (f) 81 (g) 44.5
2. (a) 20% (b) 10% (c) 15% (d) 10%
3. 40 g (b) 10 g (c) 80 g (d) 30 g (e) 50 g
4. (a) 3.13 M (b) 0.32 M (c) 0.7 M (d) 0.3 M (e) 1.02 M
5. (a) 0.4 g (b) 0.286 g (c) 584 g (d) 4990 g (e) 5.88 g
6. (a) 3.13 N (b) 0.64 N (c) 1.4 N (d) 1.5 N (e) 2.04 N
7. (a) 19.6 g (b) 0.858 g (c) 71.25 g (d) 39.2 g (e) 65.6 g
8. (a) 0.7 molal (b) 1.4 molal (c) 2.5 molal (d) 1 molal
   (e) 0.22 molal
9. (a) 1250 ml (b) 625 ml
10. (a) 2.77 ml (b) 22.2 ml (c) 66.5 ml (d) 20.8 ml
11. 197.5 ml
12. 29 ml

ANSWERS TO PROBLEMS, PAGE 100

1. 0.2
2. 0.28
3. 14.9 mm
4. 26.4 mm
5. 51.8
6. (a) 50 (b) 100.52°C
7. (a) 150 (b) -1.55°C
8. 494
9. 405
10. -10.1°C
11. 989 g
12. 3050 g

ANSWERS TO PROBLEMS, PAGE 106

1. 0.667 N
2. 0.25 N
3. (a) 0.2 N (b) 3.7 g
4. (a) 0.114 N (b) 11.2 g
5. 47.75 g
6. 27 g
7. 1.12 l.
8. (a) 0.25 N (b) 0.125 M
9. 4 liters
10. 16%

ANSWERS TO PROBLEMS, PAGE 111

1. 2400
2. 27,000
3. 4.925×10^{-3} ohms
4. 2.94 ohms
5. (a) 50 ohms (b) 200 watts
6. 44 kw-hr
7. 53.6 amperes
8. 16.6 amperes
9. 48 hrs
10. (a) 11.2 liters (b) 216 g
11. 27
12. 53.3 lb

ANSWERS TO PROBLEMS, PAGE 116

1. (a) $\dfrac{[NH_3]^2}{[N_2][H_2]^3}$ (b) $\dfrac{[NO]^2}{[N_2][O_2]}$ (c) $\dfrac{[PCl_3][Cl_2]}{[PCl_5]}$

   (d) $\dfrac{[CO_2]^2}{[CO]^2[O_2]}$ (e) $\dfrac{[H_2O]^2[Cl_2]^2}{[HCl]^4[O_2]}$

2. (a) shift to the right (e) shift to the right
   (b) shift to the left (f) shift to the left
   (c) shift to the right (g) shift to the left
   (d) shift to the left

3. (a) no effect (d) shift to the right
   (b) no effect (e) shift to the right
   (c) shift to the left (f) no effect

4. (a) shift to the right (d) shift to the left
   (b) shift to the left (e) shift to the right
   (c) shift to the left

5. 50.2

6. 0.52

7. 36.7 g

8. 503 g

ANSWERS TO PROBLEMS, PAGE 122

1. 1.85×10^{-5}
2. 6.8×10^{-7}
3. 0.086 M
4. 0.01 M
5. (a) 0.42% (b) 0.042%
6. $[H^+] = 2.1 \times 10^{-2}$ moles/l. $[OH^-] = 4.76 \times 10^{-13}$ moles/l
7. $[OH^-] = 7.1 \times 10^{-2}$ moles/l. $[H^+] = 1.4 \times 10^{-13}$ moles/l
8. 2.25×10^{-6} moles/l
9. 4.6×10^{-6}
10. 2.06×10^{-10} moles/l

ANSWERS TO PROBLEMS, PAGE 127

1. (a) 6 (b) 12 (c) 3.9 (d) 8.5 (e) 3.2
2. (a) H^+ 10^{-6} moles/l OH^- 10^{-8} moles/l
   (b) H^+ 10^{-12} moles/l OH^- 10^{-2} moles/l

(c) H^+ 0.5×10^{-2} OH^- 2.0×10^{-12}

(d) H^+ 2.5×10^{-11} moles/l OH^- 4.0×10^{-4} moles/l

(e) H^+ 1.6×10^{-5} moles/l OH^- 6.3×10^{-10} moles /l

3. (a) 2 (b) 3 (c) 2.7 (d) 2.3 (e) 3.4

4. (a) 10 (b) 11 (c) 11.3 (d) 11.7 (e) 12.5

5. (a) 4 (b) 3 (c) 4.2 (d) 1.93

ANSWERS TO PROBLEMS, PAGE 131

1. (a) $[Ag^+][Cl^-]$ (b) $[Pb^{2+}][CO_3^{2-}]$ (c) $[Ag^+]^2[CrO_4^{2-}]$
   (d) $[Ag^+]^2[CO_3^{2-}]$ (e) $[Mg^{2+}][F^-]^2$ (f) $[Sr^{2+}][F^-]^2$
   (g) $[Fe^{3+}][OH^-]^3$

2. (a) 1.1×10^{-3} (b) 5.55×10^{-9} (c) 1.67×10^{-9} (d) 2.07×10^{-15}
   (e) 3.18×10^{-7}

3. (a) 1.75×10^{-11} (b) 1.1×10^{-10} (c) 1.57×10^{-6} (d) 4.3×10^{-10}

4. (a) 1.8×10^{-3} (b) 1.1×10^{-1} (c) 8.6×10^{-13} (d) 1.3

5. 1.1×10^{-8} moles/l

6. 1.0×10^{-9} moles/l

7. $BaSO_4$

8. $PbCO_3$

9. 2.3×10^{-8} g

10. 3.6×10^{-10} g

ANSWERS TO PROBLEMS, PAGE 137

1. (a) 1625 cal. (b) 260 cal.
   (c) 291 cal. (d) 151 cal.
2. 0.0166 cal/g
3. 0.454 cal/g
4. 153,800 cal.
5. 40°C
6. 122°F
7. 181,500 cal.
8. -41,200 cal.
9. 20,460 cal.
10. 66,260 cal.

ANSWERS TO PROBLEMS, PAGE 142

1. Alpha and beta particles, gamma rays.
2. Alpha particles, mass 4 and charge 2. Beta particles, mass 0 and charge -1. Gamma rays, mass 0 and charge 0.
3. (a) Two places down the table   (b) One place ahead in the table
4. (a) The rate at which a radioactive element disintegrates is proportional to the amount remaining at any given time.

(b) The time in which half of the atoms in a given radioactive isotope will have decayed to other atoms.

5. Alpha, deuterons, protons, neutrons.

6. A stable isotope is converted to a radioactive atom by nuclear bombardment.

7. (a) $_1H^1$ (b) $_1H^1$ (c) $_0n^1$ (d) $_0n^1$ (e) $_2He^4$ (f) $_2He^4$ (g) $_{-1}e^0$

ANSWERS TO PROBLEMS, PAGE 145

1. 2.6×10^5
2. 7.0×10^{-3}
3. 4×10^4
4. 7×10^2
5. 10^{-6}
6. 3.75

7. 1.2×10^{-1}
8. 10^{-6}
9. 4.13×10^6
10. 10^2
11. 2.72×10^4
12. 6×10^1

ANSWERS TO PROBLEMS, PAGE 148

1. (a) 6 (b) 4 (c) 3 (d) 3 (e) 4 (f) 2 (g) 4 (h) 3 (i) 4 (j) 5
2. (a) 608 (b) 23.8 (c) 1.058
3. (a) 15.1 (b) 369.0 (c) 65
4. (a) 0.6 (b) 1.9 (c) 14.6
5. (a) 27.9 (b) 20.1 (c) 4

SUPPLEMENTARY PROBLEMS

I. LENGTH, MASS, TEMPERATURE, VOLUME

1. Convert 6 in. to (a) mm (b) cm (c) m. (152 mm, 15.2 cm, 0.152 m)
2. Convert 180 cm to (a) in (b) ft (c) yd. (71 in, 5.9 ft, 1.97 yd)
3. A cube has sides 3 in long. Calculate its volume in (a) c. in and (b) cc. (27 c. in, 408.6 c.c)
4. A car gasoline tank has a capacity of 16 gallons. What is its capacity in liters? (60.6 liters)
5. How many Angstroms are in 70 cm? (7.0×10^9)
6. Convert 100 km/hr to mph. (62.2)
7. Methyl alcohol boils at 65°C. Convert the boiling point to °F. (149°F)
8. The density of lead is 11.4 g per cc. What is the density in lb per c. ft? (712.5)
9. Convert 98.6°F to °C. (37°C)
10. How many microns are in (a) 30 in (b) 840 cm (c) 3 meters? (7.62×10^4, 8.4×10^6, 3×10^6)

160

II. DENSITY AND SPECIFIC GRAVITY

1. A solid has a mass of 640 g and a volume of 60 cc. Calculate its density and its specific gravity. (10.7 g per cc, 10.7)
2. Calculate the density of a solid which weighs 320 g in air and 284 g when immersed in water. (8.9 g per cc)
3. Gasoline has a density of 0.7 g per ml. What is the mass of 400 ml of the liquid? (280 g)
4. A solid weighs 450 g and has a density of 2.6 g per cc. What will the volume reading be if the solid is added to 120 ml of water in a graduated cylinder? (293 ml)
5. What is the weight of pure hydrogen sulfate (H_2SO_4) in 250 ml of a 98% solution of sulfuric acid of density 1.84 g per ml? (451 g)
6. 10 ml of concentrated nitric acid of specific gravity 1.46 and 63% pure is added to water to make a volume of 100 ml. What volume of pure hydrogen nitrate (HNO_3) is in 1 ml of the dilute solution? (0.09 g)
7. If the specific gravity of carbon tetrachloride is 1.6, what is the weight of 2.5 liters of this liquid? (4000 g)
8. A rectangular piece of metal 30 cm long, 12 cm wide, and 6 cm thick weighs 15,120 g. What will it weigh when immersed in water? (12,960 g)
9. A solid weighs 350 g when immersed in water. Its volume is 20 ml. What is the weight of the solid in air and its specific gravity? (370 g, 17.5)
10. The specific gravity of cork is 0.24. Calculate the weight of 1 c ft of cork. (15 lb)

III. GAS LAWS AND GAS DENSITY

1. The volume of a gas is 380 ml at a pressure of 640 mm mercury. If the temperature is constant, what volume does the gas occupy at a pressure of 760 mm mercury? (320 ml)
2. A gas has a volume of 250 ml at a pressure of 770 mm. What is its volume if the pressure is reduced to 750 mm? (256.7 ml)
3. A gas has a volume of 150 ml at standard conditions. What will be its volume if the temperature is raised to 20°C and the pressure is doubled? (80.5 ml)
4. At 27°C the volume of a gas is 473 ml. What is occupied by the gas at 173°C, the pressure remaining constant? (703 ml)
5. At what temperature will 40 liters of a gas expand to occupy 50 liters if the original temperature was 15°C? (87°C)
6. At 18°C and 1500 mm pressure the volume of a gas is 5 cubic feet. Calculate the volume at standard conditions of temperature and pressure. (9.1 c. ft)

7. At $18°C$ and 765 mm, 1.29 liters of a gas weighs 2.71 g. Calculate the density of the gas in grams per liter at S.T.P.   (2.8 g/l)

8. 560 ml of a gas at STP weighs 1.55 g. What is the weight of 5.0 liters of the gas at $25°C$ and 800 mm pressure?   (13.3 g)

9. The density of carbon monoxide is 3.17 g per 1 at $-20°C$ and 2.35 atm. pressure. What is the weight of 22.4 liters of the gas at STP? (28 g)

10. A cylinder can withstand an internal pressure of 20 atm. If it contains a gas at 4 atm pressure at $25°C$, at what temperature in $°C$ should the cylinder burst?   ($1217°C$)

IV. ATOMIC WEIGHT, MOLECULAR WEIGHT, MOLES

1. What is the weight in grams of 20 GAW of sodium? (Na = 23) (460 g)
2. How many atoms are in a sample of aluminum weight 1.35 g? (Al = 27 (3.0×10^{22})
3. What is the weight in grams of an atom of nitrogen? (N = 14) (2.3×10^{-22} g)
4. One atom of an element weighs 3.3×10^{-22} g. Calculate the atomic weight of the element and write its symbol. (200, Hg)
5. What is the weight of (a) 0.05 moles of helium (b) 12 moles of Na_2CO_3? (He = 4, C = 12, O = 16, Na = 23)   (0.2 g, 1272 g)
6. How many moles are represented by 7 g of KOH? (K = 39, H = 1, O = 16)   (0.125 moles)
7. Calculate the formula weight of (a) $CaCO_3$ (b) $Ca(NO_3)_2$ (c) $PbSO_4$ (100,   164,   303)
8. Calculate the formula weight of $Na_2CO_3.10H_2O$. (Na = 23, C = 12, O = 16, H = 1)   (286)
9. How many moles are in 1 liter (1 kg) of water? (H = 1, O = 16) (55.5 moles)
10. Which is heavier, 0.2 moles of H_2SO_4 or 0.5 moles of HCl? (H = 1, S = 32, O = 16, Cl = 35.5)   (0.5 moles of HCl)

V. PERCENTAGE COMPOSITION, EMPIRICAL AND MOLECULAR FORMULAS

1. What is the simplest formula of a hydrocarbon which is 85.63% carbon, and 14.37% hydrogen? (CH_2)
2. A compound is K = 26.57%, Cr = 35.36%, O = 38.07%. Calculate its empirical formula. ($K_2Cr_2O_7$)
3. What is the simplest formula of a compound with Fe = 53.73%, S = 46.27%?   (Fe_2S_3)

4. Calculate the molecular formula of a compound with carbon, 73.8%, hydrogen, 8.7%, nitrogen, 17.5%. The molecular weight is 162. ($C_{10}H_{14}N_2$)

5. A compound is 30.51% nitrogen and 69.49% oxygen. If the molecular weight is 92, calculate the true formula. (N_2O_4)

6. Calculate the percentage of oxygen in (a) $KClO_3$, (b) $KClO_4$ and (c) $K_4P_2O_7$. (a) 39.2% (b) 46.2% (c) 34%

7. An oxide of aluminum contains 52.9% Al. Calculate the empirical formula of the oxide. (Al_2O_3)

8. 77.60 g of lead form 85.6 g of lead oxide. Calculate the formula of the oxide. (Pb_3O_4)

9. 1.25 g of hydrate were heated. This compound lost 0.45 g of water. Upon analysis, the residue showed the following composition: Cu = 0.32 g, S = 0.16 g, the remainder was oxygen. Calculate the formula of the compound. ($CuSO_4 \cdot 5H_2O$)

10. A gaseons bydrocarbon is 82.8% weight carbon and 17.2% weight hydrogen. Under standard conditions 500 ml. of the gas weigh 1.29 gm. Find the simple (empirical) formula and the true (molecular) formula. (C_2H_5 ; C_4H_{10})

VI. WEIGHT AND VOLUME CALCULATIONS FROM EQUATIONS

1. What weight of calcium hydroxide is required to neutralize a solution of nitric acid which contains 25.2 g of pure hydrogen nitrate? (15.6 g)

2. What weight of copper (II) oxide is formed by the thermal decomposition of 5.6 g of copper (II) nitrate? (2.4 g)

3. In the reaction between magnesium chloride and silver nitrate, what weight of silver nitrate is necessary to make 4.78 g of silver chloride? (5.3 g)

4. What weight of hydrogen is formed by the action of hydrochloric acid on 150 g of zinc? (4.6 g)

5. What weight of iron is in 100 tons of an ore which is 85% ferric oxide? (59.5 tons)

6. How many grams of water will be formed by the reduction of 200 g of ferric oxide?

$$Fe_2O_3 \ + \ 3H_2 \longrightarrow 2Fe \ + \ 3H_2O \qquad (67.5 \text{ g})$$

7. How many liters of O_2 are required to oxidize 50 liters of NH_3?

$$(4NH_3 \ + \ 5O_2 \longrightarrow 4NO \ + \ 6H_2O) \qquad (62.5 \text{ l})$$

8. Glucose upon fermentation undergoes the following reaction:

$$C_6H_{12}O_6 \longrightarrow 2CO_2 \ + \ 2C_2H_5OH$$

Calculate the following which are obtained by the fermentation of 540 g of glucose:

(a) The weight of ethanol $(C_2H_5OH_6$ formed.   (276 g)
(b) The weight of CO_2 formed.   (264 g)
(c) The volume of CO_2 formed at STP.   (134.4 l)

9. Excess hydrochloric acid is added to 42 gm. of sodium sulphite. What weight of sodium chloride is produced? What volume of sulphur dioxide is formed at standard conditions?   (399 g; 7.47 l.)

10. A mixture of calcium hydroxide and ammonium chloride is heated 6.5 l. of ammonia gas were obtained at $120°C$ and 800 mm. pressure. What weight of ammonium chloride reacted?   (11.35 gm.)

11. What volume of oxygen is required for the conversion of 400 ml of sulfur dioxide to sulfur trioxide?   (200 ml)

12. What are the volumes of hydrogen and oxygen required to produce 80 liters of steam at $120°C$ and 700 mm pressure? (80 l H_2, 40 l O_2)

13. What is the volume composition of the gases remaining after the complete combustion of a mixture of 60 ml of acetylene (C_2H_2) and 200 ml of oxygen? Measurements are made at room conditions. (120 ml CO_2, 50 ml excess O_2)

14. How many cubic feet of air are required for the complete combustion of 100 c. ft of butane (C_4H_{10})?   (3250 c.ft)

VII. ATOMIC WEIGHTS AND SPECIFIC HEATS

1. When 2.35 g of tin is converted to its oxide, 2.985 g of the compound is formed. The specific heat of tin is 0.056. Calculate (a) the gram equivalent weight of tin   (b) the accurate atomic weight, and   (c) its valence in this oxide.   (29.6 g, 118.4, 4)

2. 8.1 g of an oxide contains 5.66 g of the metal. The specific heat of the metal is 0.113 cal/g. Calculate the accurate atomic weight of the metal.   (56.6)

3. What are the approximate atomic weights of elements with the following specific heats: (a) 0.23 (b) 0.14 (c) 0.082? (27.8, 45.7, 77.1)

VIII. EQUIVALENT WEIGHT

1. The oxide of a metal is 70% by weight metal. What is the equivalent weight of the metal?   (18.7)

2. When 0.82 gm. of a metal is converted to its oxide, 1.14 gm. of the oxide is formed. Calculate the G. E. W. of the metal.   (21 g)

3. On reduction of 1.64 of the oxide of a metal, 0.92 gm. of metal remains. What is the G. E. W. of the metal?   (10.2 g)

4. Silver bromide is 57.4% by weight silver. Calculate the equivalent weight of bromine if the equivalent of silver is 108? (82.1)

5. One chloride of phosphorus contains 1.00 gm of phosphorus combined with 3.43 gm of chlorine. What is the G.E.W. of phosphorus? (10.4 g)

6. 1.00 gm. of a metal displaces 486 ml. of hydrogen measured under standard conditions. What is the G.E.W. of the metal? (22.9 g)

7. On addition of 0.26 gm. of an active metal to excess hydrochloric acid 186 ml. of hydrogen were collected at 23°C and 768 mm. pressure. Find the equivalent of the metal? (16.8)

IX. GAS DENSITY AND GRAM MOLECULAR WEIGHT

1. Calculate the density of carbon dioxide in g. per liter at S.T.P. (C = 12, O = 16) (1.96 g. per liter)

2. (a) What is the density of acetylene C_2H_2, in gm. per liter at S.T.P.? (C = 12, H = 1)
   (b) What is the density of acetylene at 35°C and 900 mm. pressure? (1.16 g. per l., 1.22 g. per l.)

3. Under standard conditions the density of a gas is 3.17 gm. per liter. Calculate the gram molecular weight of the gas. (71.0 g)

4. At 22°C and 740 mm. pressure, 400 ml. of a gas weigh .34 gm.
   (a) What is the density of the gas in gm. per liter at S.T.P.
   (b) What is the gram molecular weight of the gas? (0.94 g per liter, 21.1 g)

5. 0.642 gm. of a gas occupies a volume of 224 ml. at 20°C and 756 mm. pressure. Calculate the gram molecular weight of the gas. (69.3 g)

X. MOLARITY AND NORMALITY

1. What weight of $Ca(OH)_2$ is present in 75 ml of a 0.05 N solution? (O.14 g)

2. A solution of H_3PO_4 contains 0.29 g of H_3PO_4 per ml. Calculate the molarity and the normality of this solution. (2.96 M, 8.87 N)

3. What is the normality and molarity of a 10.67% HNO_3 solution? The specific gravity of this solution is 1.06.) (1.8 M, 1.8 N)

4. 500 ml of NH_3 measured at 765 mm and 20°C were absorbed in 750 ml of water. (a) Assuming that the change in volume is negligible, calculate the molarity of this solution. (b) What is the normality of this solution? (0.027 M, 0.027 N)

5. What volume of concentrated HCl solution must be used to prepare 20 liters of 0.2 N solution? (Specific gravity of concentrated HCl solution is 1.19 and it contains 37.00% of HCl by weight.) (0.332 l.)

6. Calculate the weight of CuS formed by treating 400 ml of 0.25 Molar $CuSO_4$ solution with excess H_2S.   (9.56 g)

7. Calculate the volume of CO_2 liberated at S.T.P. by treating 200 ml of a 0.3 Molar solution of Na_2CO_3 with excess H_2SO_4.   (1.34 l.)

8. 15 ml of 2 N base neutralize 60 ml of an acid solution. Calculate the normality of the acid.   (0.5 N)

9. Calculate the normality of the solution formed by dissolving 50 g of $CuSO_4 \cdot 5H_2O$ in 2.5 liters of water.   (0.16 N)

10. What volume of a 36 N solution of sulfuric acid is required to make 4.5 liters of 4.0 N solution?   (0.5 liters)

11. What is the molarity of a solution containing 0.1 g of NaOH in 10 ml of solution?   (0.25 M)

12. What is the molarity of a silver nitrate solution if 25 ml of the solution react with 60 ml of a 0.5 M solution of barium chloride? (2.4 M)

1. Calculate the $[H^+]$ and the $[OH^-]$ of a solution of 0.01 M NH_4OH. K_i of NH_4OH is 1.8×10^{-5} ($[H^+] = 2.36 \times 10^{-11}$ moles/l, $[OH^-] = 4.24 \times 10^{-4}$ moles/l)

2. Calculate the $[OH^-]$ of 0.1 N HCN solution. K_i for HCN is 2.1×10^{-9} ($[OH^-] = 6.9 \times 10^{-10}$ moles/l)

3. Calculate the pH of 4 liters of 0.2 M NH_4OH to which has been added 321 g of solid NH_4Cl. K_i for NH_4OH is 1.8×10^{-5}.   (10.6)

4. Calculate the pH of 200 ml of 0.15 M HAc solution in which has been dissolved 6 g of solid NaAc. K_i for HAc is 1.85×10^{-5}.   (6.8)

5. Calculate the pH of 0.02 N base which is 4% ionized.   (10.1)

6. Calculate the pH of 300 ml of 0.05 M HCN solution to which has been added 4 g of solid NaCN. K_i for HCN is 2.1×10^{-9}.   (11.7)

7. The solubility of Ag_3PO_4 is 0.0065 g per liter. Calculate K_{sp} for Ag_3PO_4.   (5.79×10^{-20})

8. Calculate the vapor pressure of a solution that contains 100 g of sucrose ($C_{12}H_{22}O_{11}$) in 400 g of water at 20°C.   (17 mm)

9. A solution of ethyl alcohol in water freezes at -10.1°C. Calculate the percentage of the alcohol (C_2H_5OH) present in the solution. (25%)

10. What weight of ethylene glycol ($C_2H_6O_2$) must be added to 15 liters of water so that the solution will not freeze above -10°F? (11.65 Kg)

11. When 440 g of a metal were heated to 100°C and placed in 800 g of water at 25°C, the system attained temperature equilibrium at 40°C. Calculate the specific heat of the metal. (0.45 cal/g)

12. How many calories are necessary to convert 50 g of ice at -20°C to steam at 120°C?   (42,000 cal)

166

13. Calculate the heat of formation of C_4H_{10} from its elements from the following equations.

$$C_4H_{10(g)} + \frac{13}{2} O_{2(g)} \longrightarrow 4CO_{2(g)} + 5H_2O_{(g)} + 680,000 \text{ cal.}$$

$$C_{(s)} + O_{2(g)} \longrightarrow CO_{2(g)} + 94,030 \text{ cal.}$$

$$H_{2(g)} + \frac{1}{2} O_{2(g)} \longrightarrow H_2O_{(g)} + 58,000 \text{ cal.}$$

(245,880 cal)

14. Calculate the heat of reaction of:

$$C_2H_{2(g)} + 2H_{2(g)} \longrightarrow C_2H_{6(g)}$$

From the following data:

$$C_2H_{6(g)} + \frac{7}{2} O_{2(g)} \longrightarrow 2CO_{2(g)} + 3H_2O_{(\ell)} + 186,500 \text{ cal.}$$

$$C_2H_{2(g)} + \frac{5}{2} O_{2(g)} \longrightarrow 2CO_{2(g)} + H_2O_{(\ell)} + 168,300 \text{ cal.}$$

$$H_{2(g)} + \frac{1}{2} O_{2(g)} \longrightarrow H_2O_{(\ell)} + 68,400 \text{ cal.}$$

(118,600 cal)

15. Complete the following equations.

(a) $_{92}U^{238} \longrightarrow {}_{90}Th^{234} +$

(b) $_{12}Mg^{24} + {}_2He^4 \longrightarrow {}_{14}Si^{27} +$

(c) $_{18}Ar^{40} + {}_1H^1 \longrightarrow {}_0n^1 +$

(d) $_{92}U^{238} + {}_1H^2 \longrightarrow {}_{93}Np^{238} +$

(e) $_1H^2 + {}_1H^3 \longrightarrow {}_2He^4 +$

(f) $_{92}U^{235} + {}_0n^1 \longrightarrow {}_{36}Kr^{95} + {}_0n^1 +$

(g) $_7N^{15} + {}_1H^1 \longrightarrow {}_6C^{12} +$

(h) $_8O^{16} + {}_0n^1 \longrightarrow {}_6C^{13} +$

(i) $_{94}Pu^{239} + {}_2He^4 \longrightarrow {}_{96}Cm^{242} +$

(j) $_{95}Am^{241} \longrightarrow {}_{93}Np^{237} +$

(a) $_2He^4$ (b) $_0n^1$ (c) $_{19}K^{40}$ (d) 2_0n^1 (e) $_0n^1$ (f) $_{56}Ba^{140}$
(g) $_2He^4$ (h) $_2He^4$ (i) $_0n^1$ (j) $_2He^4$

NOTES

NOTES

NOTES

NOTES

NOTES

NOTES